Answer
Book

Author team

Ruth Merttens and David Kirkby

An imprint of Pearson Education Limited
Ginn is a registered trademark of Pearson Education Limited.
© Harcourt Education Ltd 2007

Acknowledgements
Every effort has been made to contact copyright holders of material reproduced
in this book. Any omissions will be rectified in subsequent printings if notice is
given to the publishers.

II 10
10 9 8 7 6

ISBN 978 0602 57571 7
British Library Cataloguing in Publication Data is available from the
British Library on request.

Published by Pearson Education, Halley Court, Jordan Hill,
Oxford OX2 8EJ
www.myprimary.co.uk
Help and support, plus the widest range of educational solutions.

Typeset by **Tech-Set Ltd**
Cover design by **Ginn and Jonathan Williams**
Cover illustration by **Per José Karlén**
Printed and bound in the UK by **Ashford Colour Press, Gosport, Hants.**

Introduction

Pupils' written work

Abacus Evolve textbooks provide clear guidance to pupils on how their work should be recorded. Pupils should be encouraged to follow this guidance, which will make marking their work substantially easier and clearly focused.

Marking pupils' work

Clearly it is important that pupils' work is seen and checked by the teacher regularly, but it is not necessary for all work to be marked by the teacher. Decisions about which work should be teacher-marked, and how it should be marked will be made alongside the need to maximise time available for teaching and guiding pupils through their activities.

A suggested approach within *Abacus Evolve* is to make these decisions Block by Block. Decide, for example, for each Block, which parts you want to mark, and which parts the pupils can mark.

Marking the 'Owls'

The 'Owls' are optional problem-solving or investigational activities for extra challenge on each page. They should generally be marked by the teacher. The pupils' responses to the 'Owls' may well vary because of the often open-ended nature of the activities, however the answers give suggestions where appropriate. Pupils should also be encouraged to use a systematic approach to solving these problems, where relevant.

For many 'Owls' you may want to ask the pupils to work in groups or pairs, possibly leading to a group display of their results.

Contents

Textbook I

Block AI

Page 3
Hundreds, tens and units

1. 561
2. 199
3. 253
4. 472
5. 606
6. 937
7. three hundred and sixty-five
8. four hundred and two
9. two hundred and seventy-nine
10. five hundred and forty-three
11. six hundred and twelve
12. one hundred and eighty-seven

Owl 963, 852, 741

Page 4
4-digit numbers

1. 1647
2. 3261
3. 6470
4. 2089
5. 5005
6. 3601
7. 7707
8. 4300
9. 6416, 6417, 6418
10. 2398, 2399, 2400
11. 4000, 4001, 4002
12. 5669, 5670, 5671
13. 1998, 1999, 2000
14. 1010, 1011, 1012

Owl 18

Page 5
4-digit numbers

1. 6470
2. 3191

3. 4862
4. 9910
5. 1200
6. 8770
7. 4600
8. 5791
9. two thousand and one
10. three thousand three hundred
11. four thousand and fourteen
12. three thousand and three
13. six thousand one hundred
14. one thousand and ninety-nine

Owl Answers may vary. Possible
     answers include: 6000 and 8000
     with middle number 7000; or 1500
     and 2500 with middle number 2000

Page 6
4-digit and 5-digit numbers

1. 1464, 1664
2. 966, 1166
3. 1392, 1592
4. 1566, 1766
5. 1712, 1912
6. 1866, 2066

Owl Answers will vary. Possible answers
     include: 1976, 2076, 2176, 2276

7. 55642
8. 72464
9. 84933
10. 36728
11. 47519
12. 66397

Page 7
3-digit numbers

1. 342
2. 489
3. 666
4. 702
5. 293

6. 717
7. 204
8. 565
9. 953
10. 848

11.

4	0	0
	6	0
		7

12.

9	0	0
	3	0
		1

13.

7	0	0
	8	0
		4

14.

6	0	0
	9	0
		7

Owl Answers will vary. Possible answers
may include: 454, 272, 111, 808,
959, 363, etc.

Page 8
4-digit and 5-digit numbers

1. 45 thousands
   3 hundreds
   4 tens
   6 units
2. 33 thousands
   6 hundreds
   0 tens
   4 units
3. 15 thousands
   7 hundreds
   1 ten
   7 units
4. 25 thousands
   0 hundreds
   2 tens
   5 units
5. 60 thousands
   1 hundred
   0 tens
   5 units
6. 32 thousands
   1 hundred
   6 tens
   6 units
7. 14 thousands
   7 hundreds
   0 tens
   9 units
8. 71 thousands
   8 hundreds
   8 tens
   0 units
9. 99 thousands
   0 hundreds
   0 tens
   1 unit
10. 82 thousands
    1 hundred
    9 tens
    0 units
11. 10 thousands
    0 hundreds
    1 ten
    0 units
12. 60 thousands
    1 hundred
    4 tens
    0 units
13. 50 thousands
    0 hundreds
    0 tens
    0 units
14. 96 thousands
    6 hundreds
    0 tens
    9 units
15. 60 004
16. 17 602
17. 80 420
18. 96 047

page 8 continued

19. 19919

Owl Answers will vary. Possible answers may include: 13013, 14014, 15015, 16016, 17017, 18018, 19019

Page 9
4-digit and 5-digit numbers

1. 1463, 1473, 1563, 2463
2. 1984, 1994, 2084, 2984
3. 1536, 1546, 1636, 2536
4. 1889, 1899, 1989, 2889
5. 1924, 1934, 2024, 2924
6. 1912, 1922, 2012, 2912
7. 2015, 2025, 2115, 3015
8. 1648, 1658, 1748, 2648
9. 1946, 1956, 2046, 2946

Owl Answers will vary. Possible answers may include: 912, 192, 291, 921, 129, 219, 1912, 1921

10. sixty-six thousand and six
11. fourteen thousand three hundred
12. twenty-three thousand and four
13. thirty-six thousand and ten
14. fifty-four thousand and twenty
15. thirty-eight thousand and thirty-six
16. ten thousand and ten
17. seventy-nine thousand three hundred
18. sixty-one thousand and fifty

Page 10
4-digit and 5-digit numbers

1. 97899, 97891, 97839, 97831, 97399, 97391, 97339, 97331, 91899, 91891, 91839, 91831, 91399, 91391, 91339, 91331, 57899, 57891, 57839, 57831, 57399, 57391, 57339, 57331, 51899, 51891, 51839, 51831, 51399, 51391, 51339, 51331

Owl 142 extra possible numbers to be made.

2. 4268, 2846
3. 4268, 3396
4. 1234
5. 3412, 1234
6. 4268, 6305
7. 1553

Page 11
Multiplying

1. $3 \times 3 = 9$
2. $4 \times 2 = 8$
3. $2 \times 5 = 10$
4. $5 \times 3 = 15$
5. $4 \times 4 = 16$
6. $6 \times 3 = 18$
7. $3 \times 4 = 12$

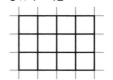

8. $2 \times 5 = 10$

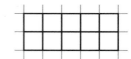

9. $4 \times 5 = 20$

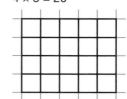

10. $6 \times 2 = 12$

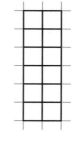

11. $5 \times 5 = 25$

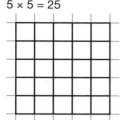

12. $3 \times 10 = 30$

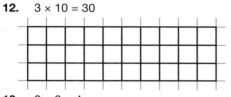

13. $2 \times 2 = 4$

14. $9 \times 2 = 18$

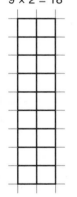

Owl Answers will vary.

Page 12
Multiplying

1. $3 \times 5 = 15$
2. $2 \times 4 = 8$

3. $3 \times 3 = 9$
4. $2 \times 6 = 12$
5. $4 \times 5 = 20$
6. $2 \times 7 = 14$
7. $3 \times 4 = 12$
8. $3 \times 6 = 18$
9. $5 \times 5 = 25$
10. $3 \times 4 = 12$

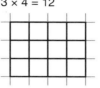

$4 \times 3 = 12$

11. $4 \times 5 = 20$

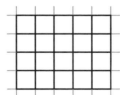

$5 \times 4 = 20$

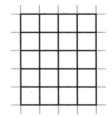

page 12 continued

12. $3 \times 5 = 15$

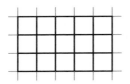

$5 \times 3 = 15$

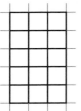

13. $2 \times 3 = 6$

$3 \times 2 = 6$

Owl

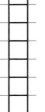

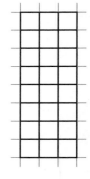
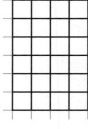

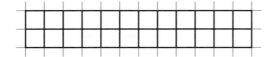

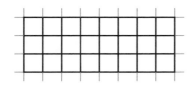

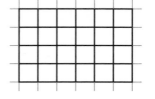

Page 13

Multiplying

1. $3 \times 10 = 30$
2. $2 \times 5 = 10$
3. $10 \times 6 = 60$
4. $4 \times 5 = 20$
5. $7 \times 2 = 14$
6. $3 \times 3 = 9$
7. $8 \times 5 = 40$
8. $1 \times 1 = 1$
9. $5 \times 7 = 35$
10. $3 \times 4 = 12$
11. $10 \times 10 = 100$
12. $20 \times 5 = 100$
13. 15p
14. 150m
15. 15p
16. 5
Owl Answers will vary. Possible answers include: $2 \times 3 \times 4$, $2 \times 2 \times 6$, $1 \times 2 \times 12$, $1 \times 1 \times 24$, $1 \times 3 \times 8$, $6 \times 1 \times 4$

Page 14

Multiplying

1. $3 \times 4 = 12$
2. $4 \times 5 = 20$
3. $1 \times 2 = 2$
4. $5 \times 6 = 30$
5. $9 \times 10 = 90$
6. $2 \times 3 = 6$
   Other numbers could include:
   $7 \times 8 = 56$
   $8 \times 9 = 72$
   $10 \times 11 = 110$
7. $3 \times 6 = 18$
8. $2 \times 7 = 14$
9. $4 \times 3 = 12$
10. $8 \times 5 = 40$
11. $7 \times 10 = 70$
12. $6 \times 5 = 30$
13. $5 \times 5 = 25$
14. $7 \times 4 = 28$

Owl Answers will vary.
15. true
16. false
17. true
18. true
19. true

Page 15

Dividing

1. $15 \div 5 = 3$
2. $8 \div 2 = 4$
3. $20 \div 5 = 4$
4. $12 \div 6 = 2$
5. $21 \div 7 = 3$
6. $20 \div 4 = 5$
7. $14 \div 2 = 7$
8. $15 \div 3 = 5$
9. $40 \div 10 = 4$
10. $40 \div 4 = 10$
11. $25 \div 5 = 5$
12. $18 \div 2 = 9$
13. $15 \div 5 = 3$
14. $21 \div 3 = 7$
15. $60 \div 10 = 6$
16. $6 \div 6 = 1$
17. $8 \div 1 = 8$
18. $16 \div 4 = 4$
Owl Answers may include: $5 \div 1 = 5$, $10 \div 2 = 5$, $15 \div 3 = 5$, $20 \div 4 = 5$, $25 \div 5 = 5$, $30 \div 6 = 5$, $35 \div 7 = 5$, $40 \div 8 = 5$

Page 16

Dividing

1. $20 \div 5 = 4$
   $20 \div 4 = 5$
2. $24 \div 6 = 4$
   $24 \div 4 = 6$
3. $30 \div 6 = 5$
   $30 \div 5 = 6$
4. $21 \div 3 = 7$
   $21 \div 7 = 3$

page 16 continued

5. $12 \div 6 = 2$
    $12 \div 2 = 6$
6. $28 \div 7 = 4$
    $28 \div 4 = 7$

Owl Answers will vary. Possible answers.

etc.

7. $27 \div 3 = 9$ teams exactly
8. $27 \div 4 = 6$ teams 3 children left over
9. $27 \div 2 = 13$ teams 1 child left over
10. $27 \div 10 = 2$ teams 7 children left over
11. $27 \div 5 = 5$ teams 2 children left over
12. $27 \div 6 = 4$ teams 3 children left over

Owl $24 \div 2 = 12$ teams, $24 \div 3 = 8$ teams, $24 \div 4 = 6$ teams, $24 \div 6 = 4$ teams, $24 \div 8 = 3$ teams, $24 \div 12 = 2$ teams.

Page 17

Dividing

1. $15 \div 4 = 3$ r 3
2. $29 \div 4 = 7$ r 1
3. $38 \div 4 = 9$ r 2
4. $22 \div 4 = 5$ r 2
5. $23 \div 5 = 4$ r 3
6. $18 \div 5 = 3$ r 3
7. $44 \div 5 = 8$ r 4
8. $36 \div 5 = 7$ r 1

Owl Answers will vary. Possible answers include 6 and 18 in the 2× and 3× tables, or 42 and 84 in the 6× and 7× tables.

9. $13 \div 3 = 4$ r 1
    5 chairs
10. $22 \div 3 = 7$ r 1
    8 chairs
11. $28 \div 3 = 9$ r 1
    10 chairs
12. $21 \div 4 = 5$ r 1
    6 cable cars

13. $43 \div 4 = 10$ r 3
    11 cable cars
14. $82 \div 4 = 20$ r 2
    21 cable cars
15. $17 \div 5 = 3$ r 2
    4 toboggans
16. $28 \div 5 = 5$ r 3
    6 toboggans
17. $61 \div 5 = 12$ r 1
    13 toboggans

Owl 60 people or any multiple of 60.

Page 18

Dividing

1. true
2. true
3. false
4. false
5. true
6. false
7. true
8. false
9. true
    $36 \div 10 = 3$ r 6
    $25 \div 3 = 8$ r 1
    $38 \div 4 = 9$ r 2
    $43 \div 5 = 8$ r 3
10. £1·80
11. 9 piles of 4, 1 pile of 2
12. 4 days with 1 slice left over
13. 38p

Explore Answers will vary. Numbers that give a remainder of 1 when divided by 2 and 3 include: 13, 19, 25, 31, 37, 43, etc. Numbers that give a remainder of 1 when divided by 2 and 5 include 11, 21, 31, 41, etc.

Block B1

Page 19

Number pairs

1. 75 cm
2. 70 cm

3. 85 cm
4. 55 cm
5. 35 cm
6. 95 cm
7. 15 cm
8. 90 cm
9. 45 cm
10. 65 cm
11. $30 + 70 = 100$
12. $25 + 75 = 100$
13. $100 - 35 = 65$
14. $40 + 60 = 100$
15. $55 + 45 = 100$
16. $85 + 15 = 100$
17. $100 - 5 = 95$
18. $20 + 80 = 100$
19. $100 - 45 = 55$
20. $100 - 10 = 90$

Owl The second person runs out of pairs first (unless you include 0 and 10, in which case the first person runs out of pairs first).

Page 20
Number pairs

1. $300\,m + 700\,m = 1000\,m$
2. $650\,m + 350\,m = 1000\,m$
3. $250\,m + 750\,m = 1000\,m$
4. $100\,m + 900\,m = 1000\,m$
5. $850\,m + 150\,m = 1000\,m$
6. $700\,m + 300\,m = 1000\,m$
7. $50\,m + 950\,m = 1000\,m$
8. $350\,m + 650\,m = 1000\,m$
9. 46 50 100
    [4] [50] $= 54$
10. 84 90 100
    [6] [10] $= 16$
11. 62 70 100
    [8] [30] $= 38$
12. 58 60 100
    [2] [40] $= 42$

13. 29 30 100
    [1] [70] $= 71$
14. 73 80 100
    [7] [20] $= 27$

Owl The pattern is that the number to add to make 100 is always made of consecutive numbers:
e.g. $22 + 78 = 100$, or $44 + 56 = 100$

Page 21
Number pairs

1. 38
2. 76
3. 64
4. 53
5. 48
6. 27
7. 44
8. 19
9. 67
10. 72
11. 61
12. 58

Explore Answers will vary. Possible answers include: $15 + 85$, $82 + 18$, $91 + 9$, any pair of 2-digit numbers where the unit digits are 5.

13. $53 + 47 = 100.$
14. $100 - 26 = 74$
15. $68 + 32 = 100$
16. $54 + 46 = 100$
17. $100 - 47 = 53$
18. $22 + 78 = 100$

Page 22
Number pairs

1. 36
2. 28
3. 46
4. 62

page 22 continued

5. 43
6. 31
7. 48
8. 33
9. 65

Owl Answers will vary. Possible answers include: 20,80; 30,70. The rule is they are multiples of 10.

10. 66
11. 73
12. 64p, 28p
13. 53

Page 23

Number pairs

1. $100p - 59p = 41p$
2. $100p - 27p = 73p$
3. $100p - 68p = 32p$
4. $100p - 18p = 82p$
5. $100p - 73p = 27p$
6. $100p - 66p = 34p$
7. $100p - 55p = 45p$
8. $100p - 83p = 17p$
9. $100p - 33p = 67p$
10. $100p - 44p = 56p$
11. $100p - 75p = 25p$
12. $100p - 65p = 35p$

Owl

1. $2 \times 20p, 1 \times 1p$
2. $1 \times 50p, 1 \times 20p, 1 \times 2p, 1 \times 1p$
3. $1 \times 20p, 1 \times 10p, 1 \times 2p$
4. $1 \times 50p, 1 \times 20p, 1 \times 10p, 1 \times 2p$
5. $1 \times 20p, 1 \times 5p, 1 \times 2p$
6. $1 \times 20p, 1 \times 10p, 2 \times 2p$
7. $2 \times 20p, 1 \times 5p$
8. $1 \times 10p, 1 \times 5p, 1 \times 2p$
9. $1 \times 50p, 1 \times 10p, 1 \times 5p \ 1 \times 2p$
10. $1 \times 50p, 1 \times 5p, 1 \times 1p$
11. $1 \times 20p, 1 \times 5p$
12. $1 \times 20p, 1 \times 10p, 1 \times 5p$
13. $£1·36 + 64p = £2$
14. $£2·24 + 76p = £3$
15. $£4·42 + 58p = £5$
16. $£5·35 + 65p = £6$
17. $£6·73 + 27p = £7$
18. $£8·56 + 44p = £9$

Page 24

Number pairs

1. $346\,cm + 54\,cm = 4\,m$
2. $338\,cm + 62\,cm = 4\,m$
3. $372\,cm + 28\,cm = 4\,m$
4. $357\,cm + 43\,cm = 4\,m$
5. $428\,cm + 72\,cm = 5\,m$
6. $464\,cm + 36\,cm = 5\,m$
7. $437\,cm + 63\,cm = 5\,m$
8. $417\,cm + 83\,cm = 5\,m$

Owl Answers will vary. Possible answers are: $242 + 58 = 300$; $202 + 98 = 300$; $212 + 88 = 300$; 222… 292. The number to be added to make 300 always has a units digit of 8.

9. $381\,cm + 19\,cm = 4\,m$
10. $555\,cm + 45\,cm = 6\,m$
11. $274\,cm + 26\,cm = 3\,m$
12. $737\,cm + 63\,cm = 8\,m$

Page 25

Number pairs

1. $3500\,m + 500\,m = 4\,km$
2. $2800\,m + 200\,m = 3\,km$
3. $4600\,m + 400\,m = 5\,km$
4. $2100\,m + 900\,m = 3\,km$
5. $3700\,m + 300\,m = 4\,km$
6. $6200\,m + 800\,m = 7\,km$
7. $4300\,m + 700\,m = 5\,km$
8. $5500\,m + 500\,m = 6\,km$

Explore For 300: 10 more turns.
For 400: 5 more turns

9. $700 - 642 = 58$
10. $184 + 16 = 200$
11. $500 - 463 = 37$
12. $300 - 277 = 23$

13. $364 + 36 = 400$
14. $600 - 558 = 42$
15. $700 - 661 = 39$
16. $400 - 384 = 16$

Page 26
Number pairs

1. £3500 + £500 = £4000
2. £1800 + £200 = £2000
3. £5250 + £750 = £6000
4. £6550 + £450 = £7000
5. £3750 + £250 = £4000
6. £1850 + £150 = £2000
7. £5350 + £650 = £6000
8. £2650 + £350 = £3000
Owl Answers will vary.
9. £8·50 + £1·50 = £10
10. £5·50 + £4·50 = £10
11. £6·75 + £3·25 = £10
12. £8·25 + £1·75 = £10
13. £6·30 + £3·70 = £10
14. £3·80 + £6·20 = £10
15. £7·40 + £2·60 = £10

Page 27
2D shapes

1. (a) triangle (b) octagon
(c) rectangle (d) hexagon
(e) pentagon (f) semi-circle
(g) circle (h) square
2. (i) quadrilateral
(l) hexagon
(m) square
(n) triangle
(o) pentagon
(p) quadrilateral
Drawings will vary.
(j) and (k) are not polygons because they have curved sides
Owl Answers will vary.

Page 28
2D shapes

1. (a) triangle
(b) square
(c) square
(d) rectangle
(e) pentagon
(f) quadrilateral
2. quadrilateral
3. triangle
4. pentagon
5. hexagon
6. octagon
7. pentagon
Drawings will vary.
Owl Answers will vary.

Page 29
2D shapes

1. b
2. c
3. a and d
4. f and i
5. e and h
6. b, c and g
Explore Answers will vary.

Page 30
Polygons

1. triangle
2. hexagon
3. rectangle
4. pentagon
5. octagon
6. hexagon
7. pentagon
8. square
9. pentagon
10. triangle
11. quadrilateral
12. octagon
Sketches will vary.
Owl Answers will vary.

Page 3I

Triangles

1. equilateral: a, e
   isosceles: b, c, d, f
2. Answers will vary.
   Possible answers.

Page 32

Triangles

1. (a) equilateral   (g) scalene
   (b) isosceles   (h) scalene
   (c) isosceles   (i) isosceles
   (d) scalene   (j) scalene
   (e) scalene   (k) equilateral
   (f) isosceles   (l) equilateral
2. Answers will vary.
   Possible answer.

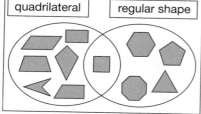

Owl Eleven triangles in all.

Page 33

Triangles

1. f
2. e
3. b
4. d
5. a
6. b, c, e and g

Owl Answers will vary.
Explore Answers will vary.

Block CI

Page 34

Centimetres and metres

1. 8 cm
2. $7\frac{1}{2}$ cm
3. 4 cm
4. $6\frac{1}{2}$ cm
5. $3\frac{1}{2}$ cm
6. 5 cm
7. $1\frac{1}{2}$ m = 150 cm
8. $1\frac{1}{4}$ m = 125 cm
9. 2 m = 200 cm
10. $1\frac{3}{4}$ m = 175 cm
11. $\frac{1}{2}$ m = 50 cm
12. $2\frac{1}{4}$ m = 225 cm

Owl Answers will vary.

Page 35

Centimetres and metres

1. 1·5 m = 150 cm
2. 3·5 m = 350 cm and   1·5 m = 150 cm
3. 0·25 m = 25 cm
4. $\frac{3}{4}$ m = 75 cm
5. 4·5 m = 450 cm
6. $\frac{1}{4}$ m = 25 cm
7. 0·2 m = 20 cm
8. 1·5 m = 150 cm
9. $2\frac{1}{4}$ m = 225 cm and $1\frac{3}{4}$ m = 175 cm
10. 125 cm = 1 m 25 cm
11. 650 cm = 6 m 50 cm
12. 330 cm = 3 m 30 cm
13. $1\frac{1}{2}$ m = 150 cm
14. $2\frac{1}{4}$ m = 225 cm
15. 3 m 15 cm = 315 cm

Owl Answers will vary.

Page 36

Millimetres

1. 7 cm 8 mm
2. 6 cm 6 mm
3. 4 cm 9 mm
4. 9 cm 3 mm
5. 64 mm = 6 cm 4 mm

6. 3 cm = 30 mm
7. 20 mm = 2 cm
8. $\frac{1}{2}$ m = 50 cm
9. 1 m = 1000 mm
10. 100 mm = 10 cm
11. 75 cm = $\frac{3}{4}$ m
12. $\frac{1}{2}$ cm = 5 mm
13. 21 cm = 210 mm
14. 150 cm = 1$\frac{1}{2}$ m
Owl Answers will vary.

Page 37
Millimetres, centimetres and metres

1. a to b: 1000 m
   b to c: 2500 m
   c to d: 750 m
   d to e: 1500 m
   d to f: 7250 m
   e to f: 5250 m
   f to g: 2250 m
   g to a: 1750 m
Owl Shortest route: a to b to c to d to
   e to f to g. Total distance: 1000 +
   2500 + 750 + 1500 + 5250 + 2250
   = 13 250 m.
2. House: metres
   Answers may vary. Possible
   answers include:
   man: metres
   dog: centimetres
   cat: centimetres
   duck: centimetres
   tractor: metres
   car: metres
   mouse: centimetres
   worm: centimetres
   beetle: millimetres
   maypole: metres

Page 38
Millimetres, centimetres and metres

1. 35 cm
   350 cm = 3 m 50 cm

2. 46 cm
   460 cm = 4 m 60 cm
3. 21 cm
   210 cm = 2 m 10 cm
4. 10 cm
   100 cm = 1 m
5. 34 cm
   340 cm = 3 m 40 cm
6. 99 cm
   990 cm = 9 m 90 cm
7. 3 miles = 5 km
8. 6 miles = 10 km
9. 30 miles = 50 km
10. 9 miles = 15 km
11. 60 miles = 100 km
12. 12 miles = 20 km
13. 1$\frac{1}{2}$ m = 150 cm
    150 cm − 60 cm = 90 cm
14. 6 × 25 cm = 150 cm
    150 cm = 1·5 m
    1·5 × 10p = 15p

Page 39
Area

1. area = 5 squares
2. area = 9 squares
3. area = 6 squares
Owl Answers will vary. Approximate
   page area 117 squares.
4. area = 14 tiles
5. area = 22 tiles
6. area = 28 tiles
   Drawings will vary.

Page 40
Area

1. 5 squares
2. 7 squares
3. 9 squares
4. 13 squares
Owl Answers will vary.
5. area = 12 squares
6. area = 9 squares

page 40 continued

7. area = 12 squares
8. area = 10 squares
9. area = 7 squares
10. area = 13 squares
    Drawings will vary.

Page 4I

Area

1. a and f
   area = 8 sq cm
   b and g
   area = 7 sq cm
   c and e
   area = $5\frac{1}{2}$ sq cm
   d has no partner
2. Drawings will vary but should have
   an area $7\frac{1}{2}$ sq cm
   a = 7 sq cm
   b = 5 sq cm
   c = $6\frac{1}{2}$ sq cm
   d = $4\frac{1}{2}$ sq cm

Owl Answers will vary.

Page 42

Tally charts and frequency tables

1. Class pets

Pets	Frequency
Cat	13
Dog	16
Rabbit	7
Hamster	9

2. Survey of favourite animals

Animal	Frequency
Chimpanzee	17
Lion	12
Giraffe	26
Shark	21
Horse	33

3. Dog
4. Rabbit
5. Horse
6. Giraffe
7. Lion
8. 45
9. 109
10. Answers will vary.
11. (a) There would be more or less
    animal votes depending on the size
    of the class.
    (b) There would be a different
    selection of animals depending on
    people's favourites.

Owl Answers will vary.

Page 43

Frequency tables

1. Cow
2. Hedgehog
3. Rabbit
4. Horse
5. Squirrel
6. Squirrel, Duck, Cow
7. Fox, Hedgehog, Horse
8. Duck
9. 71

Owl Answers will vary. Animals may
include: deer, seagull, pony.

Page 44

Frequency tables

1. Minibeasts found

Animal	Frequency
ant	27
woodlouse	11
ladybird	7
spider	3

2. ant
3. spider
4. 24
5. 4

6. 4
7. 16
8. 48
Owl ant – fourth square, woodlouse – equal first, second, third, fourth and sixth square, ladybird – equal second and fifth, spider – equal second, fourth and fifth square.

Page 45
Frequency tables

1. Frequency of vowels

Vowel	Frequency
a	15
e	18
i	8
o	11
u	5

Information written about the table will vary.

Owl b: 5, c: 2, d: 13, f: 1, g: 5, h: 6, j: 0, k: 1, l: 12, m: 1, n: 11, p: 5, q: 0, r: 11, s: 6, t: 8, v: 0, w: 2, x: 0, y: 1, z: 0. D appears most often.

Page 46
Pictograms

1. 11
2. 15
3. 9
4. 26
5. Blackbird
6. Robin
7. Robin
Owl Blackbird: 5 days, Robin: 22 days, Starling: 20 days, Blue-tit: 13 days, Chaffinch: 16

Page 47
Pictograms

1. 7
2. 3

3. 10
4. 5
5. 5
6. 4
7. blue
Owl Answers will vary.

Page 48
Pictograms

1. 9
2. 12
3. 29
4. 55
5. Tuesday and Wednesday
6. Friday and Saturday
7. 14
Explore Answers will vary.
Owl Answers will vary. As a guideline, one cow gives approximately 20 litres of milk a day, so for a herd of 100 cows, approximately 2000 litres of milk will be collected each day from a farm. Therefore, for example, one bottle could equal 100, 500 or 1000 litres.

Block DI
Page 49
Adding several numbers

1. $4 + 6 + 5 = 15$
2. $7 + 3 + 8 = 18$
3. $6 + 4 + 6 = 16$
4. $8 + 2 + 7 = 17$
5. $7 + 3 + 9 = 19$
6. $5 + 5 + 6 = 16$
Owl Answers will vary. Possible answers include: $4 + 5 + 6$; $9 + 5 + 1$; $8 + 5 + 2$.
7. $5 + 8 = 13$
$13 + 9 = 22$
8. $4 + 5 = 9$
$9 + 9 = 18$

page 49 continued

9. $3 + 8 = 11$
   $11 + 9 = 20$
10. $4 + 7 = 11$
    $11 + 9 = 20$
11. $6 + 8 = 14$
    $14 + 9 = 23$
12. $7 + 7 = 14$
    $14 + 9 = 23$
13. $8 + 8 = 16$
    $16 + 9 = 25$
14. $6 + 5 = 11$
    $11 + 9 = 20$
15. $8 + 12 = 20$
    $20 + 9 = 29$
16. $4 + 3 + 6 = 13$
    $13 + 9 = 22$
17. $7 + 4 + 3 = 14$
    $14 + 9 = 23$
18. $13 + 8 = 21$
    $21 + 9 = 30$

Page 50

Adding several numbers

1. $8 + 2 + 5 + 3 = 18$ minutes
2. $6 + 4 + 8 + 7 = 25$ minutes
3. $5 + 5 + 9 + 9 + 6 = 34$ minutes
4. $3 + 7 + 3 + 4 + 9 = 26$ minutes

Owl Answers will vary.

5. $30 + 70 + 80 + 40 = 220$
6. $50 + 50 + 60 + 80 = 240$
7. $60 + 40 + 70 + 70 = 240$
8. $80 + 20 + 70 + 30 + 40 = 240$
9. $90 + 10 + 70 + 90 = 260$
10. $70 + 30 + 60 + 90 = 250$
11. $80 + 20 + 60 + 90 = 250$
12. $60 + 40 + 80 + 50 = 230$

Page 51

Adding several numbers

1. $8 + 2 + 6 + 3 = 19$ minutes
2. $7 + 3 + 8 + 6 + 3 = 27$ minutes
3. $5 + 5 + 8 + 7 + 9 = 34$ minutes
4. $7 + 3 + 8 + 5 = 23$ minutes

5. $6 + 4 + 8 + 5 + 3 = 26$ minutes

Owl It doesn't matter what order you add the numbers.
As long as you always take away the same number, it doesn't matter what order the calculation is done in.

6. Answers will vary.

Page 52

Adding several numbers

1. $9 + 8 + 2 + 3 = 25 - 3$
2. $7 + 6 + 6 + 4 + 9 = 33 - 1$
3. $6 + 8 + 6 + 9 = 25 + 4$
4. $14 + 8 + 6 + 9 = 33 + 4$
5. $13 + 9 + 8 + 7 = 40 - 3$
6. $7 + 7 + 8 + 8 = 40 - 10$
7. $6 + 7 + 4 + 12 = 33 - 4$
8. $7 + 8 + 5 + 9 = 31 - 2$
9. $15 + 8 + 6 + 9 + 8 = 45 + 1$
10. $11 + 6 + 7 + 9 = 29 + 4$

Explore Correct: a, b, c, d, e, f. Incorrect: none. Answers may vary.

Page 53

Adding and subtracting multiples of 10

1. $14 - 6 = 8$
   $140 - 60 = 80$
2. $17 + 5 = 22$
   $170 + 50 = 220$
3. $16 - 7 = 9$
   $160 - 70 = 90$
4. $24 + 8 = 32$
   $240 + 80 = 320$
5. $12 - 5 = 7$
   $120 - 50 = 70$
6. $17 + 9 = 26$
   $170 + 90 = 260$
7. $18 + 7 = 25$
   $180 + 70 = 250$
8. $13 - 7 = 6$
   $130 - 70 = 60$
9. $15 - 8 = 7$
   $150 - 80 = 70$

10. $23 - 9 = 14$
$230 - 90 = 140$
11. $21 - 8 = 13$
$210 - 80 = 130$
12. $11 - 7 = 4$
$110 - 70 = 40$
13. Answers will vary.
Owl Red cards: $150 + 320 + 240 + 510 + 120 = 1340$. Yellow cards: $50 + 90 + 70 + 60 = 270$. Red − Yellow: $1340 - 270 = 1070$

Page 54
Adding and subtracting multiples of 10

1. Total: $310 + 70 = 380$
Difference: $310 - 70 = 240$
2. Total: $220 + 70 = 290$
Difference: $220 - 70 = 150$
3. Total: $440 + 80 = 520$
Difference: $440 - 80 = 360$
4. Total: $230 + 90 = 320$
Difference: $230 - 90 = 140$
5. Total: $340 + 60 = 400$
Difference: $340 - 60 = 280$
6. Total: $150 + 80 = 230$
Difference: $150 - 80 = 70$
7. Total: $210 + 80 = 290$
Difference: $210 - 80 = 130$

Owl
1. £3100 + £350 = £3450
2. £2200 + £350 = £2550
3. £4400 + £400 = £4800
4. £2300 + £450 = £2750
5. £3400 + £300 = £3700
6. £1500 + £400 = £1900
7. £2100 + £400 = £2500
8. $320 - 60 = 260$
9. $430 - 80 = 350$
10. $370 + 70 = 440$
11. $360 + 80 = 440$
12. $880 + 40 = 920$
13. $830 - 60 = 770$
14. $710 - 90 = 620$
15. $280 + 50 = 330$
16. $640 + 50 = 690$

Page 55
Adding and subtracting multiples of 10

1. $18 + 4 = 22$
$1800 + 400 = 2200$
2. $24 + 7 = 31$
$2400 + 700 = 3100$
3. $37 + 6 = 43$
$3700 + 600 = 4300$
4. $22 - 6 = 16$
$2200 - 600 = 1600$
5. $12 - 8 = 4$
$1200 - 800 = 400$
6. $23 - 7 = 16$
$2300 - 700 = 1600$
7. $14 + 8 = 22$
$1400 + 800 = 2200$
8. $33 - 8 = 25$
$3300 - 800 = 2500$
9. $41 - 9 = 32$
$4100 - 900 = 3200$
Owl Answers will vary. Possible answers are: 1 and 10, 2 and 11, 3 and 12, 4 and 13, 5 and 14, 6 and 15, 7 and 16, 8 and 17, 9 and 18, 10 and 19, 11 and 20, 12 and 21, 13, and 22, 14 and 23, 15 and 24.
10. Total: £210 + £390 = £600
Difference: £390 − £210 = £180
11. Difference: $480\,m - 260\,m = 220\,m$
Total: $480\,m + 260\,m = 740\,m$
12. Total: 3200 miles + 2400 miles = 5600 miles
Difference: 3200 miles − 2400 miles = 800 miles

Page 56
Adding and subtracting multiples of 10

1. $1800 + 600 = 2400$
2. $2100 - 400 = 1700$
3. $2700 + 500 = 3200$
4. $3400 - 600 = 2800$

page 56 continued

5. $1500 + 800 = 2300$
6. $2200 - 700 = 1500$
7. $2900 - 1200 = 1700$
8. $1900 + 700 = 2600$
Owl 2100 and 3000, 2200 and 3100, 2300 and 3200, 2400 and 3300, 2500 and 3400
9. £2400 + £3700 = £6100
£2400 + £4100 = £6500
£3700 + £1800 = £5500
£3700 + £1700 = £5400
£3700 + £4100 = £7800
£1800 + £4100 = £5900
£1700 + £4100 = £5800
Pairs of safes with total amounts over £5000
£4100 - £3700 = £400
£2400 - £1800 = £600
£2400 - £1700 = £700
£1800 - £1700 = £100
Pairs of safes with a difference of less than £1000: 1800–1700, 4100–3700, 2400–1800, 2400–1700

Page 57

Minutes 'past' and 'to'

minutes past the hour:
1. 21
2. 18
3. 27
4. 9
5. 32
6. 46
7. 25
8. 11
minutes to the hour:
1. 39
2. 42
3. 33
4. 51
5. 28
6. 14
7. 35

8. 49
Owl Answers will vary.
9. 10 minutes past 4
quarter past 4
19 minutes past 4
26 minutes to 5
20 minutes to 5
quarter to 5
11 minutes to 5

Page 58

Reading the time

minutes 'past' or 'to':
1. 27 minutes past 2
2. 16 minutes past 3
3. 8 minutes to 7
4. 19 minutes to 6
5. 28 minutes to 10
digital times:
1. 2:27
2. 3:16
3. 6:52
4. 5:41
5. 9:32
6. 7:55
7. 8:04
8. 10:12
9. 5:55
10. 10:30
11. 3:52
Owl Answers will vary.

Page 59

Reading the time

1. 11 minutes past 3
2. 26 minutes past 4
3. 25 minutes to 2
4. 10 minutes to 3
5. 23 minutes to 4
6. 17 minutes to 7
7. 18 minutes past 9
8. 28 minutes to 1
9. 14 minutes to 8

Owl 1:35, 2:50, 3:11, 3:37, 4:26, 6:43, 7:46, 9:18, 12:32 time gaps between each are: 1 hour 15 minutes, 21 minutes, 26 minutes, 49 minutes, 2 hours 17 minutes, 1 hour 3 minutes, 1 hour 32 minutes, 3 hours 14 minutes.

10. 6:15 pm
11. 4:08 am
12. 12:45 am
13. 12:16 pm
14. 1:48 pm
15. 12:25 am

Page 60
am and pm

1. 7:20 am
2. 8:50 pm
3. 11:35 am
4. 5:45 pm
5. 3:45 pm
6. 1:15 am
7. 8:22 am
8. Kareena gets there first and has to wait 30 minutes
9. 9:08
10. 12:28
11. 4:04
12. 8:13

Page 6I
Seconds

seconds past the minute:
1. 17 seconds
2. 23 seconds
3. 9 seconds
4. 31 seconds
5. 48 seconds
6. 52 seconds
seconds to the next minute:
1. 43 seconds
2. 37 seconds
3. 51 seconds

4. 29 seconds
5. 12 seconds
6. 8 seconds
7. 60 seconds
8. 30 seconds
9. 120 seconds
10. 300 seconds
11. 600 seconds
12. 15 seconds
Owl 330

Page 62
Seconds

1. 1 minute 38 seconds, 1 minute 54 seconds, 2 minutes 7 seconds, 2 minutes 18 seconds, 2 minutes 31 seconds, 2 minutes 38 seconds, 2 minutes 47 seconds, 3 minutes 9 seconds, 3 minutes 11 seconds
2. Gita
3. Afram
4. Anna
5. Billy, Anna, Karim, Becky, Afram
6. Lisa, Jenny, Josh
7. Jenny, Josh
8. Karim
9. $\frac{1}{2}$ minute, 40 seconds, 1 minute, 1 minute 25 seconds
10. 1 minute 20 seconds, 85 seconds, $1\frac{1}{2}$ minutes, 95 seconds
11. 125 seconds, 2 minutes 20 seconds, 145 seconds, 2 minutes 35 seconds
Owl Answers will vary. Estimates should be around the 12–20 minutes mark for 1000 seconds. 1000 seconds = 16 minutes 40 seconds. 2000 seconds = 33 minutes 20 seconds.

Page 63
Seconds

1. 215 seconds
2. 242 seconds
3. 157 seconds

page 63 continued

4. 190 seconds
5. 191 seconds
6. 175 seconds
7. 7 minutes 53 seconds or 473 seconds
8. 13 minutes 35 seconds or 815 seconds
9. 4 minutes 36 seconds or 276 seconds
10. 14 minutes 58 seconds or 898 seconds
11. 105 seconds
12. 158 seconds
13. 196 seconds
14. 249 seconds
15. 118 seconds
16. 137 seconds
17. 620 seconds
18. 335 seconds
Owl Answers will vary.

Page 64
Seconds

1. 1 minute 20 seconds
2. 1 minute 55 seconds
3. 2 minutes 15 seconds
4. 3 minutes 20 seconds
5. 6 minutes 40 seconds
6. 3 minutes 13 seconds
7. 1 minute 39 seconds
8. 3 minutes 37 seconds
9. 11 minutes 10 seconds
10. 15
11. 3 seconds
12. 93p
Explore Some answers will vary.
5 minutes = 300 seconds, half an hour = 1800 seconds, 1 hour = 3600 seconds, a school day (9:00 till 3:00) = 21 600 seconds, 1 day = 86 400 seconds, time asleep (will vary), 8 hours = 28 800 seconds

Block EI
Page 65
2s, 3s, 4s, 5s, 10s

1. 12, 14, 16, 18
2. 18, 21, 24, 27
3. 20, 24, 28, 32
4. 30, 35, 40, 45
5. 50, 60, 70, 80
Owl 24 multiples of 2 under 50, 16 multiples of 3 under 50, 12 multiples of 4 under 50, 9 multiples of 5 under 50
6. 5, 10, 15, 20, 25, 30, 35, 40, 45, 50
10, 20, 30, 40, 50, 60, 70, 80, 90, 100
10, 20, 30, 40, 50
7. 2, 4, 6, 8, 10, 12, 14, 16, 18, 20
3, 6, 9, 12, 15, 18, 21, 24, 27, 30
6, 12, 18

Page 66
Multiples

1. 40, 25, 15, 20, 10
2. 40, 12, 14, 32, 16, 20, 10, 18
3. 40, 20, 10
4. 21, 12, 15, 18
5. 40, 12, 32, 16, 20
6. 40, 41, 25, 17, 14, 32, 11, 16, 20, 10
Owl 11, 13, 17, 19, 23, 25, 29, 31
7. 200, 300, 400, 500, 600
8. 200, 225, 250, 275, 300
9. 200, 150, 100, 50, 0
10. 200, 400, 600, 800, 1000
11. 200, 190, 180, 170, 160
12. 200, 202, 204, 206, 208
13. 200, 250, 300, 350, 400
14. 200, 175, 150, 125, 100
15. 200, 198, 196, 194, 192

Page 67
Multiples

1. 28, 30
52, 54

67, 68
17, 18
9, 10
36, 38
43, 44
48, 50
87, 88
79, 80
24, 26
92, 94

2. 28, 30
52, 60
67, 70
17, 20
9, 10
36, 40
43, 50
48, 50
87, 90
79, 80
24, 30
92, 100

3. 28, 30
52, 55
67, 70
17, 20
9, 10
36, 40
43, 45
48, 50
87, 90
79, 80
24, 25
92, 95

4. 28, 50
52, 75
67, 75
17, 25
9, 25
36, 50
43, 50
48, 50
87, 100
79, 100

24, 25
92, 100

5. All 150

Owl Answers may include: 25, 75, 125, 175, 225, 275: they all end in 5. They are all 50 apart. They repeat the same pattern of ending in 25 and 75 alternately.

Explore Answers will vary. Possible answers include: The obvious pattern is the repetition of 4, 8, 2, 6, 0 … a cycle of 5 different unit digits. Another pattern is that the difference between the units digits goes 4, 6, 4, 6, 4, 6 … The ×3 table has a units digit pattern of : 3, 6, 9, 2, 5, 8, 1, 4, 7, 0 … a cycle of 10 different unit digits. The pattern of differences between the units in the ×3 table goes: 3, 3, 7, 3, 3, 7, 3, 3, 7 … The ×6 table has a units digit pattern of: 6, 2, 8, 4, 0 … a cycle of 5 different unit digits. The pattern of differences between the units in the ×6 table goes: 4, 6, 4, 4, 6 … The ×7 table has a units digit pattern of: 7, 4, 1, 8, 5, 2, 9, 6, 3, 0 … a cycle of 10 different unit digits. The pattern of differences between the units in the ×7 table goes: 3, 3, 7, 3, 3, 7, 3, 3, 3, 7 … The ×2 table has a cycle of 5 different units digits: 2, 4, 6, 8, 0 … the pattern of differences goes: 2, 2, 2, 8 … The ×8 table has a cycle of 5 different unit digits: 8, 6, 4, 2, 0 … the pattern of differences goes: 2, 2, 2, 2, 8 … The ×9 table has a pattern of 10 different units digits: 9, 8, 7, 6, 5, 4, 3, 2, 1, 0 … the pattern of differences goes: 1, 1, 1, 1, 1, 1, 1, 1, 1, 1, 9 … The ×5 table has a cycle of 2 different units digits: 5, 0 … the pattern of differences goes: 5, 5, 5, 5 …

Page 68
Multiples

1. true
2. false
3. true
4. false
5. true
6. true
7. 16 = 1 point
   21 = 3 points
   total = 4 points
8. 14 = 1 point
   25 = 2 points
   9 = 3 points
   total = 6 points
9. total = 0 points
10. 26 = 1 point
    35 = 2 points
    21 = 3 points
    total = 6 points
11. 4 = 1 point
    27 = 3 points
    3 = 3 points
    total = 7 points
12. 8 = 1 point
    28 = 1 point
    35 = 2 points
    total = 4 points
13. 10
14. 6
15. 25
16. 100
17. 20
18. 50

Page 69
Multiplication facts

1. (a) 6
   (b) 12
   (c) 18
2. (d) 20
   (e) 50
   (f) 80

3. (g) 20
   (h) 30
   (i) 35
4. (j) 3
   (k) 12
   (l) 21
5. (m) 12
   (n) 24
6. $3 \times 2 = 6$
7. $3 \times 10 = 30$
8. $4 \times 5 = 20$
9. $2 \times 4 = 8$
10. $4 \times 3 = 12$
11. $9 \times 2 = 18$
12. $6 \times 4 = 24$
13. $8 \times 5 = 40$
14. $6 \times 5 = 30$
15. $5 \times 3 = 15$
16. $7 \times 10 = 70$
17. $9 \times 4 = 36$
18. $8 \times 2 = 16$
19. $10 \times 5 = 50$
20. $8 \times 3 = 24$
21. $7 \times 2 = 14$
Owl Answers will vary.

Page 70
Multiplication and division facts

1. $18 \div 2 = 9$
2. $25 \div 5 = 5$
3. $70 \div 10 = 7$
4. $15 \div 3 = 5$
5. $20 \div 4 = 5$
6. $14 \div 2 = 7$
7. $35 \div 5 = 7$
8. $21 \div 3 = 7$
9. $32 \div 4 = 8$
10. $45 \div 5 = 9$
11. $24 \div 6 = 4$
12. $24 \div 8 = 3$
Owl 29, 28, 26, 25, 23, 22, 20, 19, 17, 16, 14, 13, 11, 10, 8, 7, 5, 4, all have remainders when divided by 3. 29, 26, 23, 20, 17, 14, 11, 8 all have a remainder of 2 when divided by 3.

13. $14 \div 2 = 7$, $14 \div 7 = 2$
14. $15 \div 5 = 3$, $15 \div 3 = 5$
15. $18 \div 6 = 3$, $18 \div 3 = 6$
16. $28 \div 7 = 4$, $28 \div 4 = 7$
17. $4 \times 5 = 20$, $5 \times 4 = 20$
18. $3 \times 4 = 12$, $4 \times 3 = 12$
19. $2 \times 4 = 8$, $4 \times 2 = 8$
20. $10 \times 5 = 50$, $5 \times 10 = 50$

Page 71
Multiplication and division facts

1. $7 \times 2 = 14$
2. $8 \times 3 = 24$
3. $20 \div 4 = 5$
4. $45 \div 5 = 9$
5. $6 \times 5 = 30$
6. $18 \div 2 = 9$
7. $24 \div 3 = 8$
8. $5 \times 3 = 15$
9. $8 \times 2 = 16$
10. $6 \times 4 = 24$
11. $12 \div 4 = 3$
12. $21 \div 3 = 7$
13. $6 \times 3 = 18$
14. $9 \times 4 = 36$
15. $32 \div 4 = 8$

Explore

1	2	3	4	5	6	7	8	9	10
2	4	6	8	10	12	14	16	18	20
3	6	9	12	15	18	21	24	27	30
4	8	12	16	20	24	28	32	36	40
5	10	15	20	25	30	35	40	45	50
6	12	18	24	30	36	42	48	54	60
7	14	21	28	35	42	49	56	63	70
8	16	24	32	40	48	56	64	72	80
9	18	27	36	45	54	63	72	81	90
10	20	30	40	50	60	70	80	90	100

Page 72
Multiplication and division facts

1. 3
2. 21

3. 4
4. 9
5. 3
6. 25
7. 1
8. $6 \times 3 = 18$
9. $14 \div 2 = 7$
10. $7 \times 5 = 35$
11. $30 \div 5 = 6$
12. $32 \div 4 = 8$
13. $7 \times 10 = 70$
14. $5 \times 4 = 20$
15. $21 \div 3 = 7$
16. $9 \times 2 = 18$
17. $7 \times 4 = 28$
18. $12 \div 2 = 6$
19. $9 \times 3 = 27$
Owl Answers will vary.

Page 73
Fractions

fraction of red candles in each set:

1. $\frac{3}{4}$
2. $\frac{2}{3}$
3. $\frac{3}{5}$
4. $\frac{5}{6}$
5. $\frac{2}{5}$
6. $\frac{3}{7}$
7. $\frac{5}{8}$
8. $\frac{2}{7}$
9. $\frac{3}{10}$

fraction of yellow candles in each set:

1. $\frac{1}{4}$
2. $\frac{1}{3}$
3. $\frac{2}{5}$
4. $\frac{1}{6}$
5. $\frac{3}{5}$
6. $\frac{4}{7}$
7. $\frac{3}{8}$
8. $\frac{5}{7}$
9. $\frac{7}{10}$

page 73 continued

Explore $\frac{1}{2}$

$\frac{1}{3}, \frac{2}{3}$

$\frac{1}{4}, \frac{2}{4}, \frac{3}{4}$

$\frac{1}{5}, \frac{2}{5}, \frac{3}{5}, \frac{4}{5}$

$\frac{1}{6}, \frac{2}{6}, \frac{3}{6}, \frac{4}{6}, \frac{5}{6}$

Page 74
Mixed numbers

1. $2\frac{1}{4}$
2. $1\frac{3}{4}$
3. $3\frac{1}{2}$
4. $1\frac{2}{3}$
5. $2\frac{1}{3}$
6. $3\frac{2}{3}$
7. $1\frac{3}{8}$
8. $2\frac{1}{8}$
9. $3\frac{7}{8}$

Owl

1. $2\frac{3}{4}$
2. $3\frac{1}{4}$
3. $1\frac{1}{2}$
4. $3\frac{1}{3}$
5. $2\frac{2}{3}$
6. $1\frac{1}{3}$
7. $3\frac{5}{8}$
8. $2\frac{7}{8}$
9. $1\frac{1}{8}$
10. $1\frac{1}{4} = \frac{5}{4}$
11. $2\frac{3}{4} = \frac{11}{4}$
12. $3\frac{1}{4} = \frac{13}{4}$
13. $5 = \frac{20}{4}$
14. $1\frac{2}{3} = \frac{5}{3}$
15. $3\frac{1}{3} = \frac{10}{3}$
16. $5\frac{2}{3} = \frac{17}{3}$
17. $3 = \frac{9}{3}$
18. $1\frac{3}{5} = \frac{8}{5}$
19. $2\frac{1}{5} = \frac{11}{5}$
20. $3\frac{4}{5} = \frac{19}{5}$
21. $6\frac{3}{5} = \frac{33}{5}$

Page 75
Mixed numbers

1. $1\frac{3}{4}$
2. $2\frac{2}{5}$
3. $3\frac{1}{3}$
4. $2\frac{5}{6}$
5. $1\frac{3}{10}$
6. $1\frac{4}{6}$ or $1\frac{2}{3}$
7. 5
8. 9
9. 16
10. 37
11. 29
12. 17

Owl Answers will vary.

13.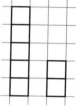

14.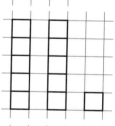

15.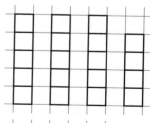

16.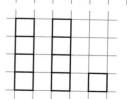

17.

18.

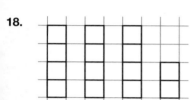

Page 76
Mixed numbers

1. $1\frac{3}{4}$
2. $1\frac{1}{4}$
3. $4\frac{3}{4}$
4. $10\frac{3}{4}$
5. $5\frac{1}{2}$
6. 17
7. $14\frac{1}{2}$
8. $8\frac{1}{2}$
9. $3\frac{1}{3}$
10. $6\frac{2}{3}$
11. $20\frac{2}{3}$
12. $8\frac{2}{3}$

Owl Ferry: 32 trips. Rowing boat: 16 trips.
Punt: 24 trips.

13. $3\frac{1}{3}$
14. $1\frac{3}{4}$
15. $2\frac{1}{2}$
16. $1\frac{4}{5}$
17. $2\frac{3}{10}$
18. $1\frac{1}{7}$
19. $10\frac{1}{2}$
20. $6\frac{1}{5}$
21. $11\frac{1}{10}$
22. $12\frac{2}{5}$

23. $2\frac{1}{6}$
24. $2\frac{5}{8}$

Page 77
Matching fractions

shaded fractions:

1. $\frac{1}{2} = \frac{2}{4}$
2. $\frac{1}{3} = \frac{2}{6}$
3. $\frac{4}{10} = \frac{2}{5}$
4. $\frac{1}{4} = \frac{2}{8}$
5. $\frac{1}{2} = \frac{3}{6}$
6. $\frac{6}{8} = \frac{3}{4}$
7. $\frac{4}{6} = \frac{2}{3}$
8. $\frac{1}{3} = \frac{3}{9}$

unshaded fractions:

1. $\frac{1}{2} = \frac{2}{4}$
2. $\frac{2}{3} = \frac{4}{6}$
3. $\frac{6}{10} = \frac{3}{5}$
4. $\frac{3}{4} = \frac{6}{8}$
5. $\frac{1}{2} = \frac{3}{6}$
6. $\frac{2}{8} = \frac{1}{4}$
7. $\frac{2}{6} = \frac{1}{3}$
8. $\frac{2}{3} = \frac{6}{9}$

Explore Answers will vary.

Page 78
Matching fractions

$a = \frac{4}{8},$ $g = \frac{1}{2}$
$b = \frac{1}{3},$ $e = \frac{2}{6}$
$c = \frac{1}{4},$ $f = \frac{2}{8}$
$d = \frac{3}{4},$ $k = \frac{6}{8}$
$h = \frac{3}{5},$ $l = \frac{6}{10}$
$i = \frac{4}{6},$ $j = \frac{2}{3}$

Owl Answers will vary.

Explore $\frac{1}{4} = \frac{2}{8}, \frac{2}{4} = \frac{4}{8}, \frac{3}{4} = \frac{6}{8}, \frac{1}{2} = \frac{4}{8}, \frac{1}{2} = \frac{3}{6},$
$\frac{1}{3} = \frac{2}{6}, \frac{2}{3} = \frac{4}{6}$

If you add cards 9 and 10:

$\frac{1}{3} = \frac{3}{9}, \frac{2}{3} = \frac{6}{9}, \frac{1}{2} = \frac{5}{10}, \frac{1}{5} = \frac{2}{10}, \frac{2}{5} = \frac{4}{10},$
$\frac{3}{5} = \frac{6}{10}, \frac{4}{5} = \frac{8}{10}$

Page 79
Matching fractions

1. $\frac{1}{2} = \frac{2}{4}$
2. $\frac{2}{4} = \frac{4}{8}$
3. $\frac{2}{2} = \frac{4}{4}$
4. $\frac{6}{8} = \frac{3}{4}$
5. $\frac{1}{2} = \frac{4}{8}$
6. $1 = \frac{4}{4}$
7. $\frac{1}{3} = \frac{2}{6}$
8. $\frac{2}{3} = \frac{4}{6}$
9. $\frac{3}{6} = \frac{6}{12}$
10. $\frac{2}{3} = \frac{8}{12}$
11. $\frac{1}{3} = \frac{4}{12}$
12. $\frac{3}{3} = \frac{6}{6}$
13. 4
14. $\frac{1}{3} = 10$ children
15. $\frac{1}{3}$

Owl

Page 80
Matching fractions

1. $\frac{1}{2}$ and $\frac{2}{4}$
   $\frac{1}{3}$ and $\frac{2}{6}$
   $\frac{1}{4}$ and $\frac{2}{8}$
   $\frac{1}{5}$ and $\frac{2}{10}$
   $\frac{1}{6}$ and $\frac{2}{12}$
   $\frac{2}{3}$ and $\frac{4}{6}$
   $\frac{2}{5}$ and $\frac{4}{10}$
   $\frac{3}{4}$ and $\frac{6}{8}$
   $\frac{3}{5}$ and $\frac{6}{10}$
   $\frac{4}{5}$ and $\frac{8}{10}$
   $\frac{5}{6}$ and $\frac{10}{12}$
   $\frac{7}{10}$ has no partner

2. $\frac{4}{6}$
3. $\frac{6}{12}$
4. $\frac{2}{6}$
5. $\frac{2}{3}$
6. $\frac{6}{20}$
7. $\frac{3}{4}$

1																			
$\frac{1}{5}$				$\frac{1}{5}$				$\frac{1}{5}$				$\frac{1}{5}$				$\frac{1}{5}$			
$\frac{1}{10}$		$\frac{1}{10}$		$\frac{1}{10}$		$\frac{1}{10}$		$\frac{1}{10}$		$\frac{1}{10}$		$\frac{1}{10}$		$\frac{1}{10}$		$\frac{1}{10}$		$\frac{1}{10}$	
$\frac{1}{20}$	$\frac{1}{20}$	$\frac{1}{20}$	$\frac{1}{20}$	$\frac{1}{20}$	$\frac{1}{20}$	$\frac{1}{20}$	$\frac{1}{20}$	$\frac{1}{20}$	$\frac{1}{20}$	$\frac{1}{20}$	$\frac{1}{20}$	$\frac{1}{20}$	$\frac{1}{20}$	$\frac{1}{20}$	$\frac{1}{20}$	$\frac{1}{20}$	$\frac{1}{20}$	$\frac{1}{20}$	$\frac{1}{20}$

Textbook 2

Block A2

Page 3
Sequences

1. 144, 146
2. 455, 425, 415
3. 442, 242
4. 401, 400, 398
5. 500, 490, 470
6. 370, 380, 390, 400
7. 6678, 5678, 4678, 3678
8. 3244, 3245, 3246, 3247
9. 4007, 3997, 3897, 3797
10. 793, 803, 813, 823
11. 8612, 8602, 8592, 8582
12. 1589, 1590, 1591, 1592
13. 963, 1063, 1163, 1263

Owl Answers will vary.

Page 4
10, 100, 1000 more and less

1. 119, 128
2. 237, 248
3. 154, 164
4. 335, 434, 435
5. 30, 140
6. 560, 670
7. 870, 970
8. 440, 540, 550
9. 3800, 4700
10. 4300, 5200
11. 3100, 3200, 4200
12. 4748, 4648, 5648
13. 2946, 3946, 3936
14. 6732, 6722, 6822
15. 7593, 6593, 6493
16. 1841, 1941, 1951

Owl Answers will vary.

Page 5
Adding and subtracting 10, 100, 1000

1–9. Answers will vary.
Owl 3890
Explore Answers will vary.

Page 6
Adding and subtracting 10, 100, 1000

1. 4832
2. 8693
3. 6742
4. 4806
5. 4807
6. 2073
7. 18085
8. 46935
9. 21701
10. All possible answers should be in the form of: X99X, e.g. 1993 or 4997.
11. 1983
12. 2096
13. 1006
14. 1076
15. 1773
16. 2765
17. Answers will vary.
18. Answers will vary.

Owl Answers will vary.

Page 7
Ordering

1. 473 < 521
2. 357 < 385
3. 5284 < 5448
4. 9376 > 9295
5. 7052 > 6983

page 7 continued

6. 4006 > 3997
7. 5367 > 5317
8. 4603 < 4652
9. 6832 > 6793
10. 9413 > 9409
Owl Answers will vary.
11. 713, 714, 715
12. 897, 898, 899, 900, 901, 902
13. 530, 531, 532, 533
14. 998, 999, 1000, 1001, 1002, 1003, 1004
15. 3829, 3830, 3831, 3832, 3833
16. 3298, 3299, 3300, 3301

Page 8
Ordering

1. 7735: v
   7721: w
   7783: y
   7767: x
   7746: z
2. 4720: d
   4350: e
   4160: c
   4540: a
   4980: b
3. 56381: s
   56345: r
   56308: t
   56369: p
   56333: q
Explore 12 numbers between 4000 and 8000 can be made. 24 numbers can be made between 55000 and 65000.

Page 9
Ordering

1. (a) £2716 (b) £6093
2. (a) £8046 (b) £8912
3. (a) £2593 (b) £2675
4. (a) £4703 (b) £4712
5. (a) £33482 (b) £35276
6. (a) £70001 (b) £71000
Owl Answers will vary.
Explore
7. 7632 or 7623
8. 1482, 1428, 1284 or 1248
9. Answers will vary.
10. Answers will vary.
11. 45386 or 45368
12. 17632 or 17623
Numbers as close to 6000 as possible:
7. 6237
8. 4821
9. 6234
10. 5987
11. 5864
12. 6123

Page 10
Ordering

1. Portsmath: 29576, 30482, 32567, 33291, 33910
   Real Mathid: 79280, 83460, 83490, 83540, 86540
   Math United: 71936, 72049, 72564, 74036, 74285
Owl
Portsmath: 32567 + 33 = 32600
               32567 + 433 = 33000
Real Mathid: 86540 + 60 = 86600
               86540 + 460 = 87000
Math United: 72564 + 36 = 72600
               72564 + 436 = 73000

2. 4740
3. 5835
4. 4800
5. 35500
6. 48000
7. 47480

Page 11
Odd or even?

1. odd
2. even

3. odd
4. even
5. even
6. even
7. odd
8. even
9. odd
10. odd
11. even
12. odd
13. 49, 51
14. 933, 935
15. 261, 263
16. 4165, 4167
17. 2867, 2869
18. 7325, 7327
19. 41 527, 41 529
20. 28 371, 28 373
21. 58, 60
22. 740, 742
23. 452, 454
24. 296, 298
25. 698, 700
26. 2612, 2614
27. 43 154, 43 156
28. 21 500, 21 502
Owl 98, 76, 54, 32, 10

Page 12
Odd or even?

1. (a) Answers will vary.
   (b) Answers will vary.
   (c) It is not possible.
2. (a) No two yellow numbers have the same total as a blue ringed number.
   (b) No two blue numbers have the same total as a blue ringed number.
   (c) Answers will vary.
Odd or even:
3. odd
4. odd
5. odd

6. odd
7. odd
8. even
9. even
10. even
11. odd
12. even
Units digit:
3. 3
4. 9
5. 3
6. 1
7. 1
8. 6
9. 6
10. 0
11. 9
12. 4
Owl Answers will vary.

Page 13
Odd or even?

1. even
2. even
3. odd
4. odd
5. even
6. odd
7. odd
8. even
9. odd
10. even
11. odd
12. even
Owl Answers will vary.
13. even
14. even
15. even
16. even
17. odd
18. even
19. even
20. odd
21. odd

page 13 continued

22. even
23. odd
24. odd

Page 14

Odd or even?

1. 5 and 7
2. 13 and 15
3. 7 and 9
4. 19 and 21
5. 9 and 11
6. 23 and 25
7. 4 and 6
8. 8 and 10
9. 14 and 16
10. 18 and 20
11. 30 and 32
12. 24 and 26
Owl 3 consecutive odd numbers always give an odd total. 3 consecutive even numbers always give an even total. Both series go up in steps of 6: e.g. 1 + 3 + 5 = 9, 3 + 5 + 7 = 15, etc.
13. 6 and 8
14. 1 and 5 or 3 and 7
15. 5 and 6
16. 3 and 9
17. 3, 5 and 7
Owl Answers will vary.

Page 15

Positive and negative numbers

1. (a) 3
   (b) -1
   (c) 8
   (d) -9
   (e) -4
2. (v) -7
   (w) 7
   (x) -14
   (y) -4
   (z) 14

3. (p) 12
   (q) -7
   (r) 43
   (s) -16
   (t) -39
4. 0, -1, -2, -3
5. -6, -7, -8, -9
6. -7, -6, -5, -4
7. 5, 0, -5, -10
8. -4, -2, 0, 2
9. 4, 0, -4, -8
10. -3, -5, -7, -9
Owl Answers will vary.

Page 16

Positive and negative numbers

1. 13°C
2. -3°C
3. 28°C
4. -14°C
5. 19°C
6. -10, -5, -3, -1, 4, 7
7. -11, -6, -2, 0, 3, 8
8. -73, -58, -37, 37, 58, 85
9. -11°C, -4°C, 0°C, 3°C, 7°C
10. -9°C, -1°C, 1°C, 7°C, 28°C
11. -64, -2, 0, 5, 64
12. Difference between smallest and largest:
6. 17
7. 19
8. 158
9. 18°C
10. 37°C
11. 128
Owl 1 and -5, 2 and -4, 3 and -3, 4 and -2, 5 and -1

Page 17

Positive and negative numbers

1. 5°C
2. -5°C

3. 30°C
4. ⁻17°C
5. 24°C
6. ⁻2°C
7. 1°C warmer
8. 29°C warmer
9. 32°C warmer
10. 29°C colder
11. 50°C colder
12. 3°C warmer
13. 4°C
14. 8°C
15. 4°C
16. 5°C
17. 26°C
18. 14°C
Owl Answers will vary.

Page 18
Positive and negative numbers

1. ⁻16°C
2. ⁻7°C
3. 4°C
4. 44°C
5. ⁻5°C
6. ⁻13°C
7. 17°C
8. ⁻2°C
9. ⁻8°C
Owl Answers will vary.
10. 27°C
11. 3°C
12. 180 minutes or 3 hours

Block B2
Page 19
Doubling and halving

1. 6
2. 14
3. 10
4. 16

5. 8
6. 18
7. 4
8. 12
9. 60
10. 80
11. 30
12. 90
13. 70
14. 100
15. 140
16. 50
Owl Answers will vary.
17. 3
18. 5
19. 8
20. 6
21. 7
22. 9
23. 20
24. 25
25. 40
26. 35
27. 15
28. 45
Owl 0

Page 20
Doubling and halving

1. 23
   40   6 = 46
2. 31
   60   2 = 62
3. 44
   80   8 = 88
4. 12
   20   4 = 24
5. 16
   20   12 = 32
6. 27
   40   14 = 54
7. 38
   60   16 = 76

8.
$$19$$
$$20 \quad 18 = 38$$

9.
$$28$$
$$40 \quad 16 = 56$$

10.
$$36$$
$$60 \quad 12 = 72$$

11.
$$49$$
$$80 \quad 18 = 98$$

12.
$$57$$
$$100 \quad 14 = 114$$

13.
$$48$$
$$20 \quad 4 = 24$$

14.
$$26$$
$$10 \quad 3 = 13$$

15.
$$46$$
$$20 \quad 3 = 23$$

16.
$$82$$
$$40 \quad 1 = 41$$

17.
$$34$$
$$15 \quad 2 = 17$$

18.
$$58$$
$$25 \quad 4 = 29$$

19.
$$76$$
$$35 \quad 3 = 38$$

20.
$$38$$
$$15 \quad 4 = 19$$

21.
$$92$$
$$45 \quad 1 = 46$$

22.
$$64$$
$$30 \quad 2 = 32$$

23.
$$72$$
$$35 \quad 1 = 36$$

24.
$$54$$
$$25 \quad 2 = 27$$

25. $2 \times £32 = £64$

26. $2 \times £48 = £96$

27. $2 \times £38 = £76$

28. $2 \times £18 = £36$

29. $2 \times £24 = £48$

Half price:

25. $£32 \div 2 = £16$

26. $£48 \div 2 = £24$

27. $£38 \div 2 = £19$

28. $£18 \div 2 = £9$

29. $£24 \div 2 = £12$

Owl

25. £160

26. £240

27. £190

28. £90

29. £120

You can find the cost of 20 of each item by doubling and then multiplying by 10, or multiplying by 10 and then doubling.

Page 21

Near doubles

1. double $34 = 68$
$35 + 34 = 69$

2. double $42 = 84$
$42 + 41 = 83$

3. double $26 = 52$
$26 + 27 = 53$

4. double $18 = 36$
$18 + 19 = 37$

5. double $23 = 46$
$23 + 22 = 45$

6. double $45 = 90$
$45 + 44 = 89$

7. double $28 = 56$
$28 + 27 = 55$

8. double $37 = 74$
$37 + 36 = 73$

9. double $46 = 92$
$46 + 47 = 93$

10. double $31 + 1$ or double $32 - 1$

11. double $15 + 1$ or double $16 - 1$

12. double $22 + 1$ or double $23 - 1$

13. double $14 + 1$ or double $15 - 1$

14. double $43 + 1$ or double $44 - 1$

15. double $26 + 1$ or double $27 - 1$

16. double $35 + 1$ or double $36 - 1$

17. double $47 + 1$ or double $48 - 1$

18. 18

19. 48
20. 14
21. 62
Owl Answers will vary.

Page 22
Doubles and halves

1. double 7 + 8
  = 14 + 8
  = 22
2. double 9 + 4
  = 18 + 4
  = 22
3. double 16 + 14
  = 32 + 14
  = 46
4. double 26 + 23
  = 52 + 23
  = 75
5. double 28 + 25
  = 56 + 25
  = 81
6. double 36 + double 32
  = 72 + 64
  = 136
7. double 35 + double 37
  = 70 + 74
  = 144
8. double 43 + double 46
  = 86 + 92
  = 178

Owl
1. 38
2. 30
3. 74
4. 121
5. 131
6. 136
7. 144
8. 178
Explore Answers will vary. 15 pairs with number cards 1–8. 23 pairs with cards 0–9

Page 23
Doubles and halves

1. 360 → 600 120 = 720
2. 180 → 200 160 = 360
3. 240 → 400 80 = 480
4. 420 → 800 40 = 840
5. 260 → 400 120 = 520
6. 370 → 600 140 = 740
7. 160 → 200 120 = 320
8. 340 → 600 80 = 680
9. 290 → 400 180 = 580
10. 43 tens → 86 tens → 860
11. 34 tens → 68 tens → 680
12. 22 tens → 44 tens → 440
13. 32 tens → 64 tens → 640
14. 45 tens → 90 tens → 900
15. 24 tens → 48 tens → 480
16. 41 tens → 82 tens → 820
17. 33 tens → 66 tens → 660
18. 28 tens → 56 tens → 560
19. 39 tens → 78 tens → 780
20. 47 tens → 94 tens → 940
21. 36 tens → 72 tens → 720
Owl Answers will vary.

Page 24
Doubles and halves

1. 440 → 800 80 = 880 miles
2. 320 → 600 40 = 640 miles

page 24 continued

3. 130
   200 ⌃ 60 = 260 miles

4. 270
   400 ⌃ 140 = 540 miles

5. 360
   600 ⌃ 120 = 720 miles

6. 280
   400 ⌃ 160 = 560 miles

7. 160
   200 ⌃ 120 = 320 miles

8. 170
   200 ⌃ 140 = 340 miles

Owl Answers will vary.

9. 480
   200 ⌃ 40 = 240 km

10. 280
    100 ⌃ 40 = 140 km

11. 520
    250 ⌃ 10 = 260 km

12. 760
    350 ⌃ 30 = 380 km

13. 380
    150 ⌃ 40 = 190 km

14. 940
    450 ⌃ 20 = 470 km

Owl 520 km, 760 km, 940 km

Page 25
Doubles and halves

1. £3400
2. £3700
3. £1800
4. £2600
5. £3050
6. £4300
7. £4700
8. £3900

Owl Car 3

Pie twice as big:
9. 6800 crabs

10. 7600 potatoes
11. 2800 l white sauce
12. 8400 g pastry
13. 9200 prawns
14. 5600 mackerel

Pie half as big:
9. 1700 crabs
10. 1900 potatoes
11. 700 l white sauce
12. 2100 g pastry
13. 2300 g prawns
14. 1400 g mackerel

Page 26
Doubles and halves

1. £3400
2. £7200
3. £4800
4. £3700
5. £2800
6. £2400
7. £8600
8. £3400

Explore Answers will vary. Both methods do give the same answer.

Page 27
Symmetry

1. Yes
2. No
3. Yes
4. No
5. No
6. Yes
7.

8.

9.

10.

11.

12.

Owl Answers will vary.

Page 28
Symmetry

1.

2.

3.

4.

5.

6.

7.

8.

Shapes with two lines of symmetry:
1, 2, 3, 5, 8
Explore Answers will vary.

Page 29
Symmetry

1. d
2. b
3. a
4. a
5. a and c
6. b
7. b
8. b
9. b
10.

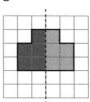

11.

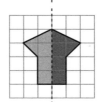

12.

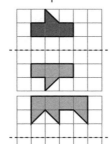

13.

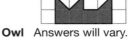

Owl Answers will vary.

Page 30
Symmetry
Explore
1. Answers will vary.
2. Answers will vary.
3. Answers will vary.
4. Answers will vary.
5.
6. Answers will vary.
7. Answers will vary.

Page 31
3D shapes
1. (a) prism
   (b) pyramid
   (c) cube
   (d) sphere
   (e) prism
   (f) cuboid
   (g) cone
   (h) cuboid
   (i) pyramid
2. triangle
3. square
4. triangle
5. rectangle
6. rectangle
7. square
Owl Answers will vary. Possible answers include: cube, cuboid, pyramid, prism.

Page 32
3D shapes
1. (a) cylinder
   (b) pyramid
   (c) prism
   (d) sphere
   (e) cuboid

Owl Answers will vary.
2. triangular face: a, b, c, e, f
   square face: c, d, e
   rectangular face: a, f
   Total number of faces:
   a has 5 faces
   b has 4 faces
   c has 5 faces
   d has 6 faces
   e has 5 faces
   f has 5 faces

Page 33
3D shapes
Shape (a)
1. prism
2. 6 vertices
3. 9 edges
4. 5 faces
Shape (b)
1. pyramid
2. 4 vertices
3. 6 edges
4. 4 faces
Shape (c)
1. cube
2. 8 vertices
3. 12 edges
4. 6 faces
Shape (d)
1. cuboid
2. 8 vertices
3. 12 edges
4. 6 faces
Shape (e)
1. cuboid
2. 8 vertices
3. 12 edges
4. 6 faces
Shape (f)
1. cylinder
2. 0 vertices
3. 2 edges
4. 3 faces

Shape (g)
1. prism
2. 12 vertices
3. 18 edges
4. 8 faces

Shape (h)
1. pyramid
2. 5 vertices
3. 8 edges
4. 5 faces

Shape (i)
1. prism
2. 10 vertices
3. 15 edges
4. 7 faces

Shape (j)
1. cube
2. 8 vertices
3. 12 edges
4. 6 faces

Shape (k)
1. cylinder
2. 0 vertices
3. 2 edges
4. 3 faces

Shape (l)
1. cone
2. 1 vertices
3. 1 edge
4. 2 faces
5. f, k, l

Owl Answers will vary.

Page 34
3D shapes

1. cube
2. pyramid
3. pyramid
4. prism
5. cuboid
6. pyramid

Explore 8, 10, 11

Block C2

Page 35
Capacity

1. (a) 250 ml
   (d) 500 ml
   (e) 100 ml
   (g) 750 ml
   (h) 600 ml

Containers that hold less than half a litre:
(a), (e)

Owl 4
2. $\frac{1}{2}$ l
3. $\frac{1}{4}$ l
4. 1 l
5. $\frac{3}{4}$ l
6. 1 l
7. 550 ml

Page 36
Capacity

1. $\frac{1}{2}$ l = 500 ml
2. $1\frac{1}{4}$ l = 1250 ml
3. $\frac{1}{4}$ l = 250 ml
4. $\frac{3}{4}$ l = 750 ml
5. $1\frac{1}{2}$ l = 1500 ml
6. $1\frac{3}{4}$ l = 1750 ml
7. 1 l = 1000 ml
8. 2 l = 2000 ml

Owl 50 and 100
9. a and h
   b and f
   c and e
   d and g

Page 37
Capacity

1. 40 days. 10 days longer
2. 67
3. 780 l
4. 250

page 37 continued

Owl 1600 seconds or 26 minutes 40 seconds

5. a and e
   b and f
   c has no match
   d and g ,

Page 38
Timetables

1. the 10:47 am
2. 9:30 am
3. the 11:35 am
4. 10:47 am
5. 5 hours 25 minutes
6. 7 hours 23 minutes

Owl

Birmingham	Crewe	Pwllheli
9:40	11:45	5:00
10:57	12:15	6:20
11:35	1:40	7:05

7. Getting up: 20 minutes
   Breakfast: 20 minutes
   Clean teeth: 5 minutes
   Travel to church hall: 15 minutes
   Meet outside church hall: 15 minutes
   Tour village: 50 minutes
   Visit school: 40 minutes
   Have tea: 1 hour 30 minutes

Owl Answers will vary.

Page 39
Timetables

1. 11:10
2. Monday, Tuesday, Wednesday, Thursday
3. 5 times
4. Art, English, RE and PE/Music

5. The first lesson every day: English and Maths
6. Longest: the first lesson every day: English and Maths
   Shortest: the second lesson every day: Maths, History/Geography, Science and CDT
7. 8 hours 15 minutes

Owl Answers will vary.

8. 2 hours 10 minutes
9. bowling
10. 30 minutes
11. the film

Page 40
Timetables

1.

Moon	Mars	Jupiter
7:15 am	11:00 am	1:00 pm
9:00 am	12:20 pm	3:40 pm
3:00 pm	7:00 pm	10:00 pm
6:00 pm	12:00 midnight	7:25 am

2. the 9:00 am
3. 7:00 pm
4. 12:00 midnight
5. the 6:00 pm
6. Answers will vary.

Page 41
Timetables

1.

Entrance	Zebras	Monkeys	Lions	Penguins
9:30	9:40	9:50	10:00	10:10
10:20	10:30	10:40	10:50	11:00
12:15	12:25	12:35	12:45	12:55
2:45	2:55	3:05	3:15	3:25
4:05	4:15	4:25	4:35	4:45

2. Answers will vary. The following table is a suggested answer.

Feed tigers	Clean tigers	Give vitamins	Provide straw	Shut tigers in
7:00 am	8:00 am	10:00 am	1:00 pm	
3:00 pm	4:00 pm	5:00 pm		6:00 pm

9. $8 + 4 = 12\,cm$
10. $12 + 10 = 22\,cm$
11. $14 + 20 = 34\,cm$
12. $16 + 6 = 22\,cm$
13. $10 + 14 = 24\,cm$
14. $8 + 5 = 13\,cm$
15. $13 + 7 = 20\,cm$
16. $5 + 19 = 24\,cm$
Owl No

Page 42
Perimeter

1. (a) 16 cm
(b) 15 cm^2
2. (a) 12 cm
(b) 8 cm^2
3. (a) 18 cm
(b) 18 cm^2
4. (a) 18 cm
(b) 14 cm^2
5. (a) 18 cm
(b) 20 cm^2
6. (a) 12 cm
(b) 9 cm^2
7. 10 m
8. 8 m
9. 10 m
10. 10 m
11. 10 m
12. 12 m
13. 12 m
14. 12 m
Owl Answers will vary.

Page 43
Perimeter

1. 48 cm
2. 57 cm
3. 30·5 cm
4. 28 cm
5. 45 cm
6. 48 cm
7. 52 cm
8. $6 + 10 = 16\,cm$

Page 44
Perimeter

1. 4 cm
2. 6 cm, 3 cm, 5·5 cm
3. 7 cm, 2 cm
Perimeter:
1. 16 cm
2. 14·5 cm
3. 18 cm
4. $5 \times 6 = 30\,cm$
5. $4 \times 4·5 = 18\,cm$
6. $6 \times 12 = 72\,cm$
7. $8 \times 9 = 72\,cm$
8. $3 \times 6.5 = 19·5\,cm$
9. $7 \times 11 = 77\,cm$
Owl Could be an octagon with 9 cm sides, a hexagon with 12 cm sides, a square with 18 cm sides or an equilateral triangle with 24 cm sides. Could also be a nonagon with 8 cm sides, or a dodecagon with 6 cm sides.

Page 45
Perimeter

1. 20 cm
2. 12 cm
3. 30 cm
4. 36 cm^2
5. 12 cm^2
6. 16 cm^2
7. (a) 12 cm
(b) 7 cm^2

8. (a) 12 cm
   (b) 6 cm²
9. (a) 16 cm
   (b) 7 cm²
10. (a) 12 cm
    (b) 5 cm²

Owl Answers will vary.
Explore Answers will vary.

Page 46
Bar graphs

1. 14
2. 5
3. 13
4. walking
5. bike
6. 19
7. 31
8. 50
9. Answers will vary.
10. Answers will vary.

Page 47
Bar graphs

1. 0·7 kg
2. 1·7 kg
3. 0·9 kg
4. 1·9 kg
5. 1·3 kg
6. 1·7 kg
7. Mondays, Tuesdays, Wednesdays, Thursdays
8. (a) 0·2 kg
   (b) 0·9 kg
9. (a) 1·7 kg
   (b) 3·2 kg
10. (a) 5 kg
    (b) 6·9 kg
11. Answers will vary.

Owl Answers will vary. Suggested answer could be that these are market days therefore more shoppers.

Page 48
Bar graphs

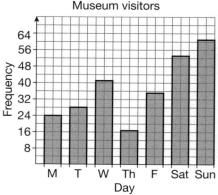
Museum visitors

1. Sunday
2. Thursday
3. 17
4. 12
5. 44
6. 7
7. 145
8. 114
9. Answers will vary. Possible reason: week days less busy because people are working or at school, etc.

Block D2

Page 49
Adding

1. 46p + 30p = 76p
2. 26p + 60p = 86p
3. 23p + 40p = 63p
4. 75p + 20p = 95p
5. 31p + 60p = 91p
6. 42p + 30p = 72p
7. 13p + 40p = 53p
8. 64p + 20p = 84p

9.

10	20	30	40	50	60	70	80	90	100
110	120	130	140	150	160	170	180	190	200
210	220	230	240	250	260	270	280	290	300
310	320	330	340	350	360	370	380	390	400
410	420	430	440	450	460	470	480	490	500

Owl Answers will vary.

Page 50
Adding

1. 70p + 30p = £1·00
5p + 6p = 11p
£1·00 + 11p = £1·11
2. 40p + 20p = 60p
7p + 5p = 12p
60p + 12p = 72p
3. 60p + 10p = 70p
5p + 7p = 12p
70p + 12p = 82p
4. 70p + 40p = £1·10
8p + 5p = 13p
£1·10 + 13p = £1·23
5. 70p + 50p = £1·20
5p + 8p = 13p
£1·20 + 13p = £1·33
6. 70p + 50p = £1·20
4p + 6p = 10p
£1·20 + 10p = £1·30
7. 80p + 70p = £1·50
4p + 5p = 9p
£1·50 + 9p = £1·59
8. £1·30 + 60p = £1·90
5p + 1p = 6p
£1·90 + 6p = £1·96
9. £1·20 + 30p = £1·50
0 + 4p = 4p
£1·50 + 4p = £1·54
10. £1·23
11. £1·66
12. £1·38
13. £1·46
14. £1·51
15. £1·25
16. £2·34
17. £2·41
Owl Answers will vary. The prices should be anywhere between 72p and 99p, e.g. 73p and 98p, or 74p and 97p, or 84p and 87p, etc.

Page 51
Adding

1. 40 + 30 + 20 = 90
5 + 6 + 4 = 15
90 + 15 = 105
2. 50 + 40 + 40 = 130
6 + 8 + 4 = 18
130 + 18 = 148
3. 20 + 70 + 30 = 120
7 + 5 + 8 = 20
120 + 20 = 140
4. 60 + 50 + 30 = 140
4 + 7 + 5 = 16
140 + 16 = 156
5. 60 + 70 + 40 = 170
3 + 7 + 2 = 12
170 + 12 = 182
6. 70 + 30 + 20 = 120
4 + 6 + 9 = 19
120 + 19 = 139
7. 50 + 20 + 40 = 110
9 + 6 + 4 = 19
110 + 19 = 129
8. 60 + 70 + 20 = 150
9 + 7 + 2 = 18
150 + 18 = 168
9. 50 + 40 + 20 = 110
7 + 9 + 9 = 25
110 + 25 = 135
10. Answers will vary.
Owl Answers will vary.

Page 52
Adding

1. Answers will vary.
Owl 387 minutes = 6 hours 27 minutes

Textbook 2

2.   £1 + £1 + £1 = £3
       40p + 30p + 50p = £1·20
       6p + 2p + 4p = 12p
                 Total = £4·32
3.   £1 + £1 + £1 = £3
       50p + 60p + 70p = £1·80
       5p + 8p + 4p = 17p
                 Total = £4·97
4.   £1 + £1 + £1 = £3
       30p + 60p + 80p = £1·70
       6p + 5p + 8p = 19p
                 Total = £4·89
5.   £1 + £1 + £1 = £3
       20p + 30p + 60p = £1·10
       7p + 3p + 4p = 14p
                 Total = £4·24
6.   £1 + £1 + £1 = £3
       30p + 70p + 20p = £1·20
       7p + 2p + 4p = 13p
                 Total = £4·33
7.   £1 + £1 + £1 = £3
       50p + 40p + 30p = £1·20
       7p + 2p + 3p = 12p
                 Total = £4·32

Page 53
Subtracting

1.   36 + 24 = 60
2.   28 + 22 = 50
3.   46 + 24 = 70
4.   34 + 26 = 60
5.   65 + 25 = 90
6.   73 + 7 = 80
7.   55 + 15 = 70
8.   29 + 31 = 60
9.   61 − 37 = 24
10.   73 − 28 = 45
11.   86 − 52 = 34
12.   58 − 23 = 35
13.   77 − 38 = 39
14.   68 − 49 = 19

15.   74 − 36 = 38
16.   56 − 39 = 17
Owl Answers will vary. For example, 50 and 85.

Page 54
Subtracting

1.   83 − 54 = 29 fish
2.   72 − 38 = 34 fish
3.   68 − 24 = 44 fish
4.   94 − 52 = 42 fish
5.   76 − 48 = 28 fish
6.   85 − 67 = 18 fish
7.   56 − 37 = 19 fish
8.   77 − 59 = 18 fish
9.   306 − 287 = 19
10.   204 − 176 = 28
11.   110 − 87 = 23
12.   301 − 275 = 26
13.   408 − 378 = 30
14.   207 − 188 = 19
15.   302 − 284 = 18
16.   111 − 96 = 15
17.   314 − 297 = 17
Owl 14

Page 55
Subtracting

1.   46p − 6p = 40p
2.   38p − 6p = 32p
3.   54p − 3p = 51p
4.   61p − 1p = 60p
5.   75p − 3p = 72p
6.   34p − 2p = 32p
7.   45p − 4p = 41p
8.   63p − 3p = 60p
9.   76p − 5p = 71p

How much each diver would have lost if they only had 10p left:

1.   36p
2.   28p
3.   44p
4.   51p

5. 65p
6. 24p
7. 35p
8. 53p
9. 66p
Owl Answers will vary. You will always end up with a units digit of 9 and a tens digit of 1 less than what you started with.
10. $84 - 16 = 68$
11. $72 - 28 = 44$
12. $63 - 27 = 36$
13. $55 - 18 = 37$
14. $73 - 36 = 37$
15. $64 - 19 = 45$
16. $58 - 29 = 29$
17. $61 - 15 = 46$
18. $74 - 26 = 48$

Page 56
Subtracting

1. $82 - 18 = 64\,cm$
2. $73 - 36 = 37\,cm$
3. $94 - 25 = 69\,cm$
4. $65 - 28 = 37\,cm$
5. $71 - 27 = 44\,cm$
6. $63 - 15 = 48\,cm$
7. $208 - 32 = 176\,cm$
8. $183 - 58 = 125\,cm$
9. $274 - 37 = 237\,cm$
Owl Answers will vary. For example, a bush 80 cm high would have 40 cm cut off to make it half the height, then 20 cm to make it half the height again, then 10 cm, then 5 cm then 2·5 cm, etc.
10. $183 - 47 = 136$
11. $221 - 188 = 33$
12. $144 - 86 = 58$
13. $164 - 55 = 109$
14. $214 - 187 = 27$
15. $372 - 136 = 236$
    $372 - 47 = 325$

Page 57
Adding and subtracting

1. $75p - 20p = 55p$
   $55p + 1p = 56p$
2. $68p - 30p = 38p$
   $38p + 1p = 39p$
3. $57p - 20p = 37p$
   $37p + 1p = 38p$
4. $63p - 30p = 33p$
   $33p + 1p = 34p$
5. $78p - 20p = 58p$
   $58p + 1p = 59p$
6. $54p - 30p = 24p$
   $24p + 1p = 25p$
7. $46p + 30p = 76p$
   $76p - 1p = 75p$
8. $56p + 10p = 66p$
   $66p - 1p = 65p$
9. $74p + 20p = 94p$
   $94p - 1p = 93p$
10. $28p + 60p = 88p$
    $88p - 1p = 87p$
11. $45p + 40p = 85p$
    $85p - 1p = 84p$
12. $63p + 30p = 93p$
    $93p - 1p = 92p$
Owl Answers will vary.

Page 58
Adding and subtracting

1. $138 + 39 = 177$ bricks
2. $125 + 49 = 174$ bricks
3. $243 + 29 = 272$ bricks
4. $176 + 19 = 195$ bricks
5. $136 + 69 = 205$ bricks
6. $217 + 39 = 256$ bricks
7. $87 - 29 = 58$
8. $133 - 41 = 92$
9. $256 - 19 = 237$
10. $84 - 39 = 45$
11. $300 - 49 = 251$
12. $110 - 31 = 79$
Owl Answers will vary.

13. 47 minutes
14. £252
15. 43 miles
16. 185 m

Page 59

Adding and subtracting

1. 246 – 59 = 187 miles
2. 427 – 79 = 348 miles
3. 154 – 88 = 66 miles
4. 285 – 79 = 206 miles
5. 274 – 57 = 217 miles
6. 164 – 89 = 75 miles
7. (a) 247 – 39 = 208 cm
    (b) 247 – 67 = 180 cm
    (c) 247 – 99 = 148 cm
    (d) 247 – 128 = 119 cm
    (e) 247 – 189 = 58 cm
Owl Answers will vary.

Page 60

Adding and subtracting

1. £179 + £29 = £208
2. £245 – £58 = £187
3. £157 + £39 = £196
4. £161 – £39 = £122
5. £222 – £59 = £163
6. £260 + £37 = £297
7. 147 and 89
8. 266 and 159
9. 266 and 333
10. 89 and 129
11. 89 and 333
12. 159 and 147
Owl Answers will vary.

Page 61

Adding

1. 40 + 30 + 7 + 8 =
     70 + 15 = 85
2. 50 + 40 + 4 + 7 =
     90 + 11 = 101

3. 60 + 70 + 2 + 4 =
     130 + 6 = 136
4. 30 + 60 + 6 + 8 =
     90 + 14 = 104
5. 70 + 80 + 5 + 7 =
     150 + 12 = 162
6. 50 + 70 + 3 + 1 =
     120 + 4 = 124
7. Children should also include
estimates.

```
  H T U
  5 6 3
+   8 8
  ─────
    1 1
  1 4 0
  5 0 0
  ─────
  6 5 1
```

8.
```
  H T U
  6 4 2
+   7 6
  ─────
      8
  1 1 0
  6 0 0
  ─────
  7 1 8
```

9.
```
  H T U
  5 8 4
+ 1 7 7
  ─────
    1 1
  1 5 0
  6 0 0
  ─────
  7 6 1
```

10.
```
  H T U
  6 8 4
+ 2 7 7
  ─────
    1 1
  1 5 0
  8 0 0
  ─────
  9 6 1
```

11.
```
  H T U
  4 7 9
+ 3 5 4
  ─────
    1 3
  1 2 0
  7 0 0
  ─────
  8 3 3
```

Textbook 2

12.
```
  H T U
  6 4 8
+ 2 5 6
    1 4
    9 0
  8 0 0
  9 0 4
```

Owl Answers will vary. For 636, answer should be 562 + 74, or any combination thereof, e.g. 572 + 64. For 609, answer should be 562 + 47, or any combination thereof. For 312, answer should be 247 + 65 or any combination thereof.

Page 62
Adding

Children should also include estimates.

1.
```
  H T U
  4 3 7
+ 1 4 6
  5 8 3 g
```

2.
```
  H T U
  3 7 8
+ 1 6 6
  5 4 4 g
```

3.
```
  H T U
  5 2 6
+ 2 1 9
  7 4 5 g
```

4.
```
  H T U
  3 5 9
+ 1 7 6
  5 3 5 g
```

5.
```
  H T U
  4 6 8
+ 1 2 9
  5 9 7 g
```

6.
```
  H T U
  3 3 6
+ 1 5 8
  4 9 4 g
```

7. Answers will vary.

Owl Answers will vary. Possible answers include: 176 + 324 = 500, 174 + 326 = 500.

Page 63
Adding

Children should also include estimates.

1.
```
    1 6 8
      7 2
  +   8 6
    3 2 6 cm
    2 1
```

2.
```
    1 5 4
      6 5
  +   2 3
    2 4 2 cm
    1 1
```

3.
```
    1 7 6
      5 4
  +   3 9
    2 6 9 cm
    1 1
```

4.
```
    1 6 5
      3 8
  +   4 6
    2 4 9 cm
    1 1
```

5.
```
    1 5 9
      7 8
  +   2 4
    2 6 1 cm
    1 2
```

Owl 74 + 63 + 52 = 189

6. 579 miles

7. 450 days. Today's date is 26th March (as long as it isn't a leap year, in which case today's date will be 25th March)

8. 1328 g or 1 kg 328 g

Textbook 2 (side tab)

Page 64

Adding

1.   Answers will vary.

Explore £555 + £467 + £459 = £1481
£555 + £467 + £386 = £1408
£555 + £459 + £386 = £1400
£555 + £467 + £368 = £1390
£555 + £459 + £368 = £1382
£467 + £459 + £386 = £1312
£555 + £386 + £368 = £1309
£467 + £459 + £368 = £1294
£467 + £386 + £368 = £1221
£459 + £386 + £368 = £1213

Block E2

Page 65

Sixes

1. $3 \times 6 = 18$
2. $5 \times 6 = 30$
3. $2 \times 6 = 12$
4. $7 \times 6 = 42$
5. $10 \times 6 = 60$
6. $8 \times 6 = 48$
7. $6 \times 6 = 36$
8. $9 \times 6 = 54$
9. $4 \times 6 = 24$
Owl 42 and 48
10. $18 \div 6 = 3$ boxes
11. $30 \div 6 = 5$ boxes
12. $54 \div 6 = 9$ boxes
13. $36 \div 6 = 6$ boxes
14. $24 \div 6 = 4$ boxes
15. $42 \div 6 = 7$ boxes

Page 66

Sixes

1.

3s	3	6	9	12	15	18	21	24	27	30
6s	6	12	18	24	30	36	42	48	54	60

2.

1s	1	2	3	4	5	6	7	8	9	10
5s	5	10	15	20	25	30	35	40	45	50
6s	6	12	18	24	30	36	42	48	54	60

3.

2s	2	4	6	8	10	12	14	16	18	20
4s	4	8	12	16	20	24	28	32	36	40
6s	6	12	18	24	30	36	42	48	54	60

Owl

6s	6	12	18	24	30	36	42	48	54	60
12s	12	24	36	48	60	72	84	96	108	120

4. $4 \times 3 = 12$, $4 \times 6 = 24$
5. $7 \times 3 = 21$, $7 \times 6 = 42$
6. $9 \times 3 = 27$, $9 \times 6 = 54$
7. $11 \times 3 = 33$, $11 \times 6 = 66$
8. $3 \times 6 = 18$
9. $8 \times 6 = 48$
10. $2 \times 6 = 12$
11. $5 \times 6 = 30$
12. $6 \times 6 = 36$
13. $20 \times 6 = 120$

Page 67

Sixes

1.   24
2.   36
3.   18
4.   54
5.   12
6.   30
7.   42
8.   48
9.   7 bags 5 left over
10.   58p
11.   54 days
Owl Answers will vary.
12. $36 \div 6 = 6$
13. $18 \div 6 = 3$
14. $42 \div 6 = 7$
15. $12 \div 6 = 2$
16. $54 \div 6 = 9$

17. $60 \div 6 = 10$
18. $24 \div 6 = 4$
19. $30 \div 6 = 5$
20. $48 \div 6 = 8$
21. 7
22. 20

Page 68
Sixes

1. $5 \times 6 = 30$
2. $7 \times 6 = 42$
3. $18 \div 6 = 3$
4. $36 \div 6 = 6$
5. $2 \times 6 = 12$
6. $9 \times 6 = 54$
7. $60 \div 6 = 10$
8. $24 \div 6 = 4$
9. $3 \times 6 = 18$
10. $8 \times 6 = 48$
11. $6 \div 6 = 1$
12. $54 \div 6 = 9$
13. $48 \div 6 = 8$
14. $4 \times 6 = 24$
15. 180
16. 360
17. 240
18. 540
19. $7 \times 60 = 420$
20. $2 \times 60 = 120$
21. $9 \times 60 = 540$
22. $3 \times 60 = 180$
23. $120 \div 60 = 2$
24. $360 \div 60 = 6$
25. $4 \times 60 = 240$
26. $480 \div 60 = 8$
27. $300 \div 60 = 5$

Page 69
Eights

1. $4 \times 8 = 32$
2. $3 \times 8 = 24$
3. $5 \times 8 = 40$
4. $6 \times 8 = 48$
5. $8 \times 8 = 64$
6. $7 \times 8 = 56$
7. $16 \div 8 = 2$ boats
8. $48 \div 8 = 6$ boats
9. $56 \div 8 = 7$ boats
10. $24 \div 8 = 3$ boats
11. $32 \div 8 = 4$ boats
12. $80 \div 8 = 10$ boats
Owl
7. 3 boats 2 spaces left
8. 8 boats
9. 10 boats 4 spaces left
10. 4 boats
11. 6 boats 4 spaces left
12. 14 boats 4 spaces left

Page 70
Eights

1. 40
2. 24
3. 32
4. 48
5. 72
6. 56
7. $4 \times 8 = 32$
8. $6 \times 8 = 48$
9. $9 \times 8 = 72$
10. $3 \times 8 = 24$
11. $8 \times 8 = 64$
12. $2 \times 8 = 16$
Owl 5 and 10 fingers show multiples of ten. 6 hands needed to show 240.
13. $2 \times 8 = 16$
14. $7 \times 8 = 56$
15. $5 \times 8 = 40$
16. $32 \div 8 = 4$
17. $11 \times 8 = 88$
18. $64 \div 8 = 8$
19. $6 \times 8 = 48$
20. $9 \times 8 = 72$
21. $0 \times 8 = 0$
22. $24 \div 8 = 3$
23. $8 \div 8 = 1$
24. $20 \times 8 = 160$

Page 7I
Eights

1.

4s	4	8	12	16	20	24	28	32	36	40
8s	8	16	24	32	40	48	56	64	72	80

2.

3s	3	6	9	12	15	18	21	24	27	30
5s	5	10	15	20	25	30	35	40	45	50
8s	8	16	24	32	40	48	56	64	72	80

3.

2s	2	4	6	8	10	12	14	16	18	20
6s	6	12	18	24	30	36	42	48	54	60
8s	8	16	24	32	40	48	56	64	72	80

Owl

8s	8	16	24	32	40	48	56	64	72	80
16s	16	32	48	64	80	96	112	128	144	160
32s	32	64	96	128	160	192	224	256	288	320

4. $5 \times 8 = 40$
5. $4 \times 8 = 32$
6. $9 \times 8 = 72$
7. $7 \times 8 = 56$
8. $2 \times 8 = 16$
9. $12 \times 8 = 96$
10. 6
11. 18

Page 72
Eights

1. $3 \times 8 = 24$
2. $5 \times 8 = 40$
3. $16 \div 8 = 2$
4. $80 \div 8 = 10$
5. $7 \times 8 = 56$
6. $4 \times 8 = 32$
7. $48 \div 8 = 6$
8. $24 \div 8 = 3$
9. $9 \times 8 = 72$
10. $8 \times 8 = 64$
11. $32 \div 8 = 4$
12. $8 \div 8 = 1$
13. $10 \times 8 = 80$
14. $20 \times 8 = 160$
15. $24 \div 8 = 3$

Explore Multiples of 8 units digits: 8, 6, 4, 2, 0. Multiples of 16 units digits: 6, 2, 8, 4, 0. They are the same digits but in a different order. The multiples of 16 units digits are the same as the multiples of 4 units digits but in the reverse order.

16. $3 \times 80 = 240$
17. $6 \times 80 = 480$
18. $5 \times 80 = 400$
19. $4 \times 80 = 320$
20. $7 \times 80 = 560$
21. $9 \times 80 = 720$
22. $160 \div 80 = 2$
23. $400 \div 80 = 5$
24. $640 \div 80 = 8$

Page 73
Ordering fractions

1. $\frac{1}{3}, \frac{3}{4}$
2. $\frac{3}{5}, \frac{2}{3}$
3. $\frac{1}{4}, \frac{2}{5}$
4. $\frac{1}{2}, \frac{5}{6}$
5. $\frac{2}{4}, \frac{5}{8}$
6. $\frac{4}{5}, \frac{7}{8}$
7. $\frac{1}{2}, \frac{3}{5}$
8. $\frac{3}{8}, \frac{2}{3}$
9. $\frac{1}{3}, \frac{1}{2}, \frac{2}{3}$
10. $\frac{1}{4}, \frac{2}{3}, \frac{3}{4}$
11. $\frac{2}{5}, \frac{2}{4}, \frac{4}{5}$
12. $\frac{1}{5}, \frac{2}{6}, \frac{5}{6}$
Owl Answers will vary.

Page 74
Ordering fractions

1. $\frac{1}{3} < \frac{1}{2}$
2. $\frac{2}{3} < \frac{3}{4}$
3. $\frac{3}{5} < \frac{5}{6}$
4. $\frac{1}{4} < \frac{2}{5}$
5. $\frac{3}{8} < \frac{1}{2}$
6. $\frac{4}{5} < \frac{7}{8}$

Owl $\frac{1}{4}, \frac{1}{3}, \frac{3}{8}, \frac{2}{5}, \frac{1}{2}, \frac{1}{2}, \frac{3}{5}, \frac{2}{3}, \frac{3}{4}, \frac{4}{5}, \frac{5}{6}, \frac{7}{8}$

7. $\frac{1}{2} < \frac{2}{3}$
8. $\frac{1}{3} > \frac{1}{4}$
9. $\frac{2}{3} < \frac{3}{4}$
10. $\frac{2}{4} = \frac{1}{2}$
11. $\frac{1}{4} < \frac{1}{2}$
12. $\frac{2}{3} > \frac{2}{4}$
13. $\frac{1}{3} < \frac{5}{12}$
14. $\frac{7}{12} < \frac{2}{3}$
15. $\frac{5}{6} > \frac{2}{3}$
16. $\frac{1}{6} < \frac{1}{3}$
17. $\frac{3}{6} = \frac{6}{12}$
18. $\frac{5}{6} < \frac{11}{12}$
19. $\frac{2}{3} = \frac{8}{12}$
20. $\frac{3}{12} > \frac{1}{6}$
21. $\frac{4}{6} = \frac{2}{3}$

Page 75
Ordering fractions

1. $\frac{1}{5}, \frac{1}{3}, \frac{2}{4}, \frac{3}{5}, \frac{2}{3}$
2. $\frac{1}{4}, \frac{1}{3}, \frac{2}{5}, \frac{2}{4}, \frac{4}{5}$
3. $\frac{2}{8}, \frac{1}{3}, \frac{3}{6}, \frac{3}{4}, \frac{7}{8}$
4. $\frac{1}{4}, \frac{2}{5}, \frac{1}{2}, \frac{3}{4}, \frac{4}{5}$
5. $\frac{1}{6}, \frac{3}{8}, \frac{2}{3}, \frac{3}{4}, \frac{5}{6}$
6. $\frac{1}{8}, \frac{3}{8}, \frac{2}{4}, \frac{5}{8}, \frac{2}{3}$
7. $\frac{2}{5}, \frac{1}{2}, \frac{3}{5}, \frac{2}{3}, \frac{3}{4}$
8. $\frac{1}{8}, \frac{1}{3}, \frac{2}{4}, \frac{5}{8}, \frac{2}{3}$
9. $\frac{1}{6}, \frac{1}{3}, \frac{3}{4}, \frac{4}{5}, \frac{7}{8}$

Owl Answers will vary. possible answers include: $\frac{2}{3}, \frac{3}{5}, \frac{4}{6}, \frac{5}{7}, \frac{5}{8}, \frac{6}{9}, \frac{7}{12}, \frac{8}{12}$

Explore Answers will vary.

Page 76
Ordering fractions

1. $\frac{1}{4}$
2. $\frac{3}{4}$
3. $\frac{3}{6}$
4. $\frac{4}{2}$
5. $\frac{6}{8}$
6. $\frac{1}{3}$

Owl Answers will vary.

7. 1, 2
8. 1, 2, 3, 4, 5
9. 1
10. 1, 2
11. 4, 5
12. 8
13. 5, 6, 7
14. 1, 2
15. 1
16. 1, 2
17. 1
18. 2

Page 77
Tenths

1. $\frac{3}{10}$
2. $\frac{7}{10}$
3. $\frac{2}{10}$
4. $\frac{6}{10}$
5. $\frac{9}{10}$
6. $\frac{8}{10}$
7. $\frac{2}{10}$

Each fraction expressed as a decimal:

1. 0·3
2. 0·7
3. 0·2
4. 0·6
5. 0·9
6. 0·8
7. 0·2
8. 0·6, $\frac{7}{10}$, eight-tenths
9. 0·3, four-tenths, $\frac{5}{10}$
10. seven-tenths, $\frac{8}{10}$, 0·9
11. $\frac{3}{10}$, 0·5, 0·7

page 77 continued

12. $\frac{5}{10}$, 0·6, $\frac{8}{10}$

13. $\frac{3}{10}$, 0·4, $\frac{1}{2}$

Owl Answers will vary.

Page 78

Tenths

1. $1\frac{3}{10}$

2. $3\frac{4}{10}$

3. $2\frac{6}{10}$

4. $1\frac{9}{10}$

5. $1\frac{7}{10}$

6. $2\frac{1}{10}$

As decimals:

1. 1·3

2. 3·4

3. 2·6

4. 1·9

5. 1·7

6. 2·1

7. $\frac{13}{10}$

8. $\frac{21}{10}$

9. $\frac{36}{10}$

10. $\frac{44}{10}$

11. $\frac{117}{10}$

12. $\frac{35}{10}$

13. $\frac{12}{10}$

14. $\frac{23}{10}$

15. $\frac{17}{10}$

16. $\frac{75}{10}$

17. $\frac{6}{10}$

18. $\frac{43}{10}$

Owl $\frac{6}{10}, \frac{12}{10}, \frac{13}{10}, \frac{17}{10}, \frac{21}{10}, \frac{23}{10}, \frac{35}{10}, \frac{36}{10}, \frac{43}{10}, \frac{44}{10}, \frac{75}{10}, \frac{117}{10}$

Answers will vary.

Page 79

Tenths

1. (a) 1·8   (b) 3·1
    (c) 1·3   (d) 0·2
    (e) 2·8   (f) 3·5
    (g) 0·6   (h) 2·4

2. 2·3 tubs

3. 4·7 tubs

4. 1·6 tubs

5. 3·8 tubs

6. 5·4 tubs

7. 7·9 tubs

For a complete number of tubs:

2. 7 more tokens

3. 3 more tokens

4. 4 more tokens

5. 2 more tokens

6. 6 more tokens

7. 1 more token

Explore Six numbers can be made between 3·3 and 7·3. Twelve numbers can be made in all.

Page 80

Tenths

1. 3·4 kg

2. 4·6 kg

3. 1·7 kg

4. 7·3 kg

5. 2·9 kg

6. 5·1 kg

Weight in grams:

1. 3400 g

2. 4600 g

3. 1700 g

4. 7300 g

5. 2900 g

6. 5100 g

Owl Answers will vary. Suggestions for animals weighing 10 times heavier: 17 kg baby seal; 29 kg cat; 34 kg small dog; 46–51 kg goat; 73 kg medium-sized dog

7. 2·0

8. 1·5

9. 3·6

10. 2·8

11. 2·1

12. 2·7

13. 2·5

14. 4·2

Block A3

Page 3
Rounding

1. 80 cm
2. 50 cm
3. 30 cm
4. 60 cm
5. 20 cm
6. 70 cm
7. 50 cm
8. 40 cm
9. 90 cm

Owl
1. 3 jumps
2. 5 jumps
3. 7 jumps
4 4 jumps
5. 9 jumps
6. 4 jumps
7. 5 jumps
8. 6 jumps
9. 3 jumps
10. a: 33→30
    b: 36→40
    c: 39→40
11. d: 71→70
    e: 74→70
    f: 77→80
12. g: 162→160
    h: 165→170
    i: 166→170
    j: 168→170

Owl 35, 36, 37, 38, 39,
41, 42, 43, and 44

Page 4
Rounding

1. 360 g 400 g
2. 280 g 300 g
3. 140 g 100 g
4. 430 g 400 g

Owl The total weight of the rabbits is
1210 g so 790 g less than 2 kg.

5. (a) 236 g→200 g
   (b) 236 g→240 g
6. (a) 347 g→300 g
   (b) 347 g→350 g
7. (a) 188 g→200 g
   (b) 188 g→190 g
8. (a) 425 g→400 g
   (b) 425 g→430 g
9. (a) 634 g→600 g
   (b) 634 g→630 g
10. (a) 857 g→900 g
    (b) 857 g→860 g

Owl The rabbit could be any weight
between 650 g and 749 g.
His sister could be any weight
between 515 g and 524 g.

Page 5
Rounding

1. c: 865; d:891
2. a: 815
3. g: 1156
4. e: 1122; f:1135
5. b: 846
6. e: 1122
7. 200 + 40
8. 380 − 160
9. 60 × 470
10. 890 ÷ 30
11. £5 + £18

Owl Answers will vary.
Possible answers include any
number from 225 to 234 added to
any number from 65 to 74.

Page 6

Rounding

1. (a) £3·87→£4
   (b) £3·87→£3·90
2. (a) £4·65→£5
   (b) £4·65→£4·70
3. (a) £9·86→£10
   (b) £9·86→£9·90
4. (a) £4·93→£5
   (b) £4·93→£4·90
5. (a) £5·46→£5
   (b) £5·46→£5·50
6. (a) £7·38→£7
   (b) £7·38→£7·40
7. (a) £6·08→£6
   (b) £6·08→£6·10
8. (a) £11·44→£11
   (b) £11·44→£11·40
9. (a) £31·64→£32
   (b) £31·64→£31·60
10. (a) £48·59→£50
    (b) £48·59→£48·60

Owl

1. (a) 200
   (b) 195
2. (a) 250
   (b) 235
3. (a) 500
   (b) 495
4. (a) 250
   (b) 245
5. (a) 250
   (b) 275
6. (a) 350
   (b) 370
7. (a) 300
   (b) 305
8. (a) 550
   (b) 570
9. (a) 1600
   (b) 1580
10. (a) 2500
    (b) 2430

11. Unrounded total: £12.57
    Rounded total:
    £12·60
    Better off with rounded prices.
    For 10 of everything:
    Unrounded total: £125·70
    Rounded total: £126·00
    Better off with rounded prices.

Owl apples; olive oil; and Super Wash

Page 7

Multiplying by 10 and 100

1. 450 m
2. 380 m
3. 620 m
4. 740 m
5. 280 m
6. 1040 m
7. 960 m
8. 650 m
9. 190 m

After 100 laps:

1. 4500 m
2. 3800 m
3. 6200 m
4. 7400 m
5. 2800 m
6. 10 400 m
7. 9600 m
8. 6500 m
9. 1900 m

Owl Hedgehogs:
1, 3, 4, 6, 7 and 8

10. $35 \times 10 = 350$
11. $47 \times 100 = 4700$
12. $280 \times 10 = 2800$
13. $360 \times 100 = 36\,000$
14. $7 \times 100 = 700$
15. $64 \times 10 = 640$
16. $68 \times 100 = 6800$
17. $11 \times 100 = 1100$
18. $49 \times 10 = 490$

Page 8

Dividing by 10 and 100

1. $4800p \div 100 = £48$
2. $750 \div 10 = £75$
3. $6400p \div 100 = £64$
4. $800p \div 100 = £8$
5. $4600 \div 10 = £460$
6. $770 \div 10 = £77$
7. $690 \div 10 = £69$
8. $9800 \div 10 = £980$
9. $7400p \div 100 = £74$
Owl 10p a day = £36·50
$£3$ a month = £36·00
10p a day is better.
10. $840 \div 10 = 84$
11. $5600 \div 100 = 56$
12. $7600 \div 10 = 760$
13. $7900 \div 100 = 79$
14. $48\,000 \div 100 = 480$
15. $85\,000 \div 100 = 850$
16. $950 \div 10 = 95$
17. $480 \div 10 = 48$
18. $8000 \div 10 = 800$

Page 9

Multiplying and dividing by 5 and 20

1. $10 \times 43p = 430p$
   $= £4·30$
2. $10 \times 65p = 650p$
   $= £6·50$
3. $10 \times 51p = 510p$
   $= £5·10$
4. $10 \times 38p = 380p$
   $380p \times 2 = 760p$
   $= £7·60$
5. $10 \times 48p = 480p$
   $480p \times 2 = 960p$
   $= £9·60$
6. $10 \times 32p = 320p$
   $320 \div 2 = 160p$
   $= £1·60$

7. True
8. False
9. True
10. False
11. £20
12. £200
13. £4000
14. £40
15. £1000
16. £400

Page 10

Multiplying and dividing

1. 39
2. £260

Explore

3. Multiply by 10 and then by 5
4. Multiply by 100 and then double it
5. Multiply by 10 and then add the number
6. Multiply by 10 and then subtract the number
   $43 \times 50 = 2150$
   $43 \times 200 = 8600$
   $43 \times 11 = 473$
   $43 \times 9 = 387$
   $18 \times 50 = 900$
   $18 \times 200 = 3600$
   $18 \times 11 = 198$
   $18 \times 9 = 162$
   $160 \times 50 = 8000$
   $160 \times 200 = 32\,000$
   $160 \times 11 = 1760$
   $160 \times 9 = 1440$
7. $73 \times 10 = 730$
8. $42 \times 100 = 4200$
9. $3900 \div 100 = 39$
10. $860 \times 10 = 8600$
11. $47 \times 5 = 235$
12. $960 \div 20 = 48$
13. $28 \times 50 = 1400$
14. $8600 \div 200 = 43$
15. $32 \times 200 = 6400$
16. $3800 \div 50 = 76$

Page II

Subtracting

1. 363   370   400
       7   30 = 37 cm

2. 126   130   200
       4   70 = 74 cm

3. 284   290   300
       6   10 = 16 cm

4. 378   380   400
       2   20 = 22 cm

5. 436   440   500
       4   60 = 64 cm

6. 152   160   200
       8   40 = 48 cm

Owl Answers will vary.
Possible examples include:
1 and 100
2 and 101
69 and 168
97 and 196
423 and 522
2764 and 2863
The units digits always differ by 1, the tens digit is always the same, the hundreds digits differ by 1.

7. 127   130   192
       3   62 = 65 cm

8. 235   240   281
       5   41 = 46 cm

9. 128   130   182
       2   52 = 54 cm

10. 216   220   274
        4   54 = 58 cm

11. 368   370   391
        2   21 = 23 cm

12. 136   140   205
        4   65 = 69 cm

Page I2

Subtracting

1. 362 – 178 = 184 cm
2. 314 – 167 = 147 cm
3. 224 – 88 = 136 cm
4. 241 – 176 = 65 cm
5. 341 – 142 = 199 cm
6. 264 – 96 = 168 cm
7. Anjilee needs to save another £284, or £342 with insurance.
8. Nick has 270 feet yet to climb. He will climb 484 feet in total.

Owl Answers will vary.
Possible examples include:
321 – 123 = 198
654 – 456 = 198
987 – 789 = 198
The answer is always 198.

Page I3

Subtracting

Children should also include estimates.

1.
```
    6 3 2
  - 3 7 5
          5 → 3 8 0
        2 0 → 4 0 0
      2 3 2 → 6 3 2
      2 5 7
```

2.
```
    3 4 1
  - 1 5 4
          6 → 1 6 0
        4 0 → 2 0 0
      1 4 1 → 3 4 1
      1 8 7
```

3.
```
    4 1 8
  - 2 4 2
          8 → 2 5 0
        5 0 → 3 0 0
      1 1 8 → 4 1 8
      1 7 6
```

4.
```
    5 2 7
  - 3 1 4
          6 → 3 2 0
        8 0 → 4 0 0
      1 2 7 → 5 2 7
      2 1 3
```

5.
```
    4 9 2
  - 3 5 6
          4 → 3 6 0
        4 0 → 4 0 0
        9 2 → 4 9 2
      1 3 6
```

6.
```
    3 9 7
  - 1 2 3
          7 → 1 3 0
        7 0 → 2 0 0
      1 9 7 → 3 9 7
      2 7 4
```

7. $325 - 187 = 138$
8. $162 - 88 = 74$
9. $243 - 168 = 75$
10. $525 - 377 = 148$
11. $613 - 366 = 247$
12. $457 - 239 = 218$
Owl Answers will vary.
An example might be: 200 m and
323 m; difference = 123 m

Page 14

Subtracting

Children should also
include estimates.
Answers can be in any order.

1.
```
    7 1 2
  - 3 4 5
          5 → 3 5 0
        5 0 → 4 0 0
      3 1 2 → 7 1 2
      3 6 7
```

2.
```
    7 1 2
  - 1 7 9
          1 → 1 8 0
        2 0 → 2 0 0
      5 1 2 → 7 1 2
      5 3 3
```

3.
```
    7 1 2
  - 2 6 8
          2 → 2 7 0
        3 0 → 3 0 0
      4 1 2 → 7 1 2
      4 4 4
```

4.
```
    7 1 2
  - 5 3 4
          6 → 5 4 0
        6 0 → 6 0 0
      1 1 2 → 3 9 7
      1 7 8
```

5.
```
    5 3 4
  - 3 4 5
          5 → 3 5 0
        5 0 → 4 0 0
      1 3 4 → 5 3 4
      1 8 9
```

6.
```
    5 3 4
  - 1 7 9
          1 → 1 8 0
        2 0 → 2 0 0
      3 3 4 → 5 3 4
      3 5 5
```

7.
```
    5 3 4
  - 2 6 8
          2 → 2 7 0
        3 0 → 3 0 0
      2 3 4 → 5 3 4
      2 6 6
```

8.
```
    3 4 5
  - 1 7 9
        1 →  1 8 0
      2 0 →  2 0 0
    1 4 5 →  3 4 5
    1 6 6
```

9.
```
    3 4 5
  - 2 6 8
        2 →  2 7 0
      3 0 →  3 0 0
      4 5 →  3 4 5
      7 7
```

10.
```
    2 6 8
  - 1 7 9
        1 →  1 8 0
      2 0 →  2 0 0
      6 8 →  2 6 8
      8 9
```

Check by adding:

1.
```
    3 4 5
  + 3 6 7
    7 1 2
    1 1
```

2.
```
    1 7 9
  + 5 3 3
    7 1 2
    1 1
```

3.
```
    2 6 8
  + 4 4 4
    7 1 2
    1 1
```

4.
```
    5 3 4
  + 1 7 8
    7 1 2
    1 1
```

5.
```
    3 4 5
  + 1 8 9
    5 3 4
    1 1
```

6.
```
    1 7 9
  + 3 5 5
    5 3 4
    1 1
```

7.
```
    2 6 8
  + 2 6 6
    5 3 4
    1 1
```

8.
```
    1 7 9
  + 1 6 6
    3 4 5
    1 1
```

9.
```
    2 6 8
  +   7 7
    3 4 5
    1 1
```

10.
```
    1 7 9
  +   8 9
    2 6 8
    1 1
```

Explore
$$873 - 545 = 328$$
$$745 - 417 = 328$$
$$545 - 217 = 328$$

Page 15
Subtracting

Children should also include estimates.

1.
```
   7 3 =   7 0 + 3 = 6 0 + 1 3
 - 4 7 = - 4 0 + 7 = 4 0 +    7
                     2 0 +    6 = 2 6
```

2.
```
   6 1 =   6 0 + 1 = 5 0 + 1 1
 - 4 3 = - 4 0 + 3 = 4 0 +    3
                     1 0 +    8 = 1 8
```

3.
```
   8 2 =   8 0 + 2 = 7 0 + 1 2
 - 5 8 = - 5 0 + 8 = 5 0 +    8
                     2 0 +    4 = 2 4
```

4.
```
   7 1 =   7 0 + 1 = 6 0 + 1 1
 - 3 8 = - 3 0 + 8 = 3 0 +    8
                     3 0 +    3 = 3 3
```

5.

$$
\begin{array}{r}
6\,2 = \quad 6\,0 + 2 = 5\,0 + 1\,2 \\
-\,2\,7 = -\,2\,0 + 7 = 2\,0 + \quad 7 \\
\hline
3\,0 + \quad 5 = 3\,5
\end{array}
$$

6.

$$
\begin{array}{r}
7\,4 = \quad 7\,0 + 4 = 6\,0 + 1\,4 \\
-\,4\,6 = -\,4\,0 + 6 = 4\,0 + \quad 6 \\
\hline
2\,0 + \quad 8 = 2\,8
\end{array}
$$

7.

$$
\begin{array}{r}
6\,5 = \quad 6\,0 + 5 = 5\,0 + 1\,5 \\
-\,1\,8 = -\,1\,0 + 8 = 1\,0 + \quad 8 \\
\hline
4\,0 + \quad 7 = 4\,7
\end{array}
$$

8.

$$
\begin{array}{r}
5\,3 = \quad 5\,0 + 3 = 4\,0 + 1\,3 \\
-\,2\,6 = -\,2\,0 + 6 = 2\,0 + \quad 6 \\
\hline
2\,0 + \quad 7 = 2\,7
\end{array}
$$

Owl Answers will vary.
An example might be:
13 and 26; 26 − 13 = 13
The larger number is double the
smaller number. The larger number
is always even.

9. In any order, six of:
82 − 74 = 8
82 − 65 = 17
82 − 57 = 25
82 − 38 = 44
74 − 65 = 9
74 − 57 = 17
74 − 38 = 36
65 − 57 = 8
65 − 38 = 27
57 − 38 = 19

Page 16
Subtracting

Children should also include estimates.

1.

$$
\begin{array}{r}
4\,2\,6 = \quad 3\,0\,0 + 1\,2\,0 + 6 \\
-\,3\,3\,3 = -\,3\,0\,0 + \quad 3\,0 + 3 \\
\hline
9\,0 + 3 = 9\,3
\end{array}
$$

2.

$$
\begin{array}{r}
5\,4\,1 = \quad 5\,0\,0 + 3\,0 + 1\,1 \\
-\,3\,3\,3 = -\,3\,0\,0 + 3\,0 + \quad 3 \\
\hline
2\,0\,0 + \quad 0 + 8 = 2\,0\,8
\end{array}
$$

3.

$$
\begin{array}{r}
6\,2\,8 = \quad 5\,0\,0 + 1\,2\,0 + 8 \\
-\,3\,3\,3 = -\,3\,0\,0 + \quad 3\,0 + 3 \\
\hline
2\,0\,0 + \quad 9\,0 + 5 = 2\,9\,5
\end{array}
$$

4.

$$
\begin{array}{r}
4\,1\,7 = \quad 3\,0\,0 + 1\,1\,0 + 7 \\
-\,3\,3\,3 = -\,3\,0\,0 + \quad 3\,0 + 3 \\
\hline
8\,0 + 4 = 8\,4
\end{array}
$$

5.

$$
\begin{array}{r}
5\,2\,2 = \quad 4\,0\,0 + 1\,1\,0 + 1\,2 \\
-\,3\,3\,3 = -\,3\,0\,0 + \quad 3\,0 + 3 \\
\hline
1\,0\,0 + \quad 8\,0 + 9 = 1\,8\,9
\end{array}
$$

6.

$$
\begin{array}{r}
6\,4\,2 = \quad 6\,0\,0 + \quad 3\,0 + 1\,2 \\
-\,3\,3\,3 = -\,3\,0\,0 + \quad 3\,0 + 3 \\
\hline
3\,0\,0 + \quad 0\,0 + 9 = 3\,0\,9
\end{array}
$$

Subtracting 251:

1.

$$
\begin{array}{r}
4\,2\,6 = \quad 3\,0\,0 + 1\,2\,0 + 6 \\
-\,2\,5\,1 = -\,2\,0\,0 + \quad 5\,0 + 1 \\
\hline
1\,0\,0 + \quad 7\,0 + 5 = 1\,7\,5
\end{array}
$$

2.

$$
\begin{array}{r}
5\,4\,1 = \quad 4\,0\,0 + 1\,4\,0 + 1 \\
-\,2\,5\,1 = -\,2\,0\,0 + \quad 5\,0 + 1 \\
\hline
2\,0\,0 + \quad 9\,0 + 0 = 2\,9\,0
\end{array}
$$

3.

$$
\begin{array}{r}
6\,2\,8 = \quad 5\,0\,0 + 1\,2\,0 + 8 \\
-\,2\,5\,1 = -\,2\,0\,0 + \quad 5\,0 + 1 \\
\hline
3\,0\,0 + \quad 7\,0 + 7 = 3\,7\,7
\end{array}
$$

4.

$$
\begin{array}{r}
4\,1\,7 = \quad 3\,0\,0 + 1\,1\,0 + 7 \\
-\,2\,5\,1 = -\,2\,0\,0 + \quad 5\,0 + 1 \\
\hline
1\,0\,0 + \quad 6\,0 + 6 = 1\,6\,6
\end{array}
$$

5.

$$
\begin{array}{r}
5\,2\,2 = \quad 4\,0\,0 + 1\,2\,0 + 2 \\
-\,2\,5\,1 = -\,2\,0\,0 + \quad 5\,0 + 1 \\
\hline
2\,0\,0 + \quad 7\,0 + 1 = 2\,7\,1
\end{array}
$$

6.

$$
\begin{array}{r}
6\,4\,2 = \quad 5\,0\,0 + 1\,4\,0 + 2 \\
-\,2\,5\,1 = -\,2\,0\,0 + \quad 5\,0 + 1 \\
\hline
3\,0\,0 + \quad 9\,0 + 1 = 3\,9\,1
\end{array}
$$

7. 53 cards
8. 166 miles
9. 142 g
10. 74 cm,
    39 cm less than half
Owl 8 times, with 32 left

Page 17
Subtracting

Children should also include estimates.

1.

$$
\begin{array}{r}
3\ 4\ 6\ =\ 2\ 0\ 0\ +\ 1\ 4\ 0\ +\ 6 \\
-\ \ \ 8\ 4\ =\ -\ \ \ \ \ \ \ \ \ \ \ \ 8\ 0\ +\ 4 \\
\hline
2\ 0\ 0\ +\ \ \ 6\ 0\ +\ 2\ =\ 2\ 6\ 2
\end{array}
$$

2.

$$
\begin{array}{r}
2\ 4\ 8\ =\ 1\ 0\ 0\ +\ 1\ 4\ 0\ +\ 8 \\
-\ \ \ 7\ 3\ =\ -\ \ \ \ \ \ \ +\ \ \ 7\ 0\ +\ 3 \\
\hline
1\ 0\ 0\ +\ \ \ 7\ 0\ +\ 5\ =\ 1\ 7\ 5
\end{array}
$$

3.

$$
\begin{array}{r}
1\ 2\ 6\ =\ 1\ 2\ 0\ +\ 6 \\
-\ \ \ 6\ 2\ =\ -\ \ \ 6\ 0\ +\ 2 \\
\hline
6\ 0\ +\ 4\ =\ 6\ 4
\end{array}
$$

4.

$$
\begin{array}{r}
4\ 8\ 2\ =\ 4\ 0\ 0\ +\ 7\ 0\ +\ 1\ 2 \\
-\ \ \ 7\ 6\ =\ -\ \ \ \ \ \ \ \ \ \ 7\ 0\ +\ \ \ 6 \\
\hline
4\ 0\ 0\ +\ \ \ 0\ +\ \ \ 6\ =\ 4\ 0\ 6
\end{array}
$$

5.

$$
\begin{array}{r}
3\ 3\ 5\ =\ 2\ 0\ 0\ +\ 1\ 3\ 0\ +\ 5 \\
-\ \ \ 8\ 2\ =\ -\ \ \ \ \ \ \ \ \ \ \ \ 8\ 0\ +\ 2 \\
\hline
2\ 0\ 0\ +\ \ \ 5\ 0\ +\ 3\ =\ 2\ 5\ 3
\end{array}
$$

6.

$$
\begin{array}{r}
1\ 3\ 7\ =\ 1\ 3\ 0\ +\ 7 \\
-\ \ \ 8\ 5\ =\ -\ \ \ 8\ 0\ +\ 5 \\
\hline
5\ 0\ +\ 2\ =\ 5\ 2
\end{array}
$$

7.

$$
\begin{array}{r}
2\ 2\ 7\ =\ 1\ 0\ 0\ +\ 1\ 2\ 0\ +\ 7 \\
-\ \ \ 6\ 4\ =\ -\ \ \ \ \ \ \ \ \ \ 6\ 0\ +\ 4 \\
\hline
1\ 0\ 0\ +\ \ \ 6\ 0\ +\ 3\ =\ 1\ 6\ 3
\end{array}
$$

8.

$$
\begin{array}{r}
1\ 2\ 4\ =\ \ 1\ 1\ 0\ +\ 1\ 4 \\
-\ \ \ 8\ 6\ =\ -\ \ \ 8\ 0\ +\ \ \ 6 \\
\hline
3\ 0\ +\ \ \ 8\ =\ 3\ 8
\end{array}
$$

9. 115 pages
10. 214 pages
11. 316 pages
12. 427 pages
13. 345 pages
14. 436 pages
Owl Answers will vary.

Page 18
Subtracting

Children should also include estimates.

1.

$$
\begin{array}{r}
2\quad {}^{1}4 \\
\cancel{3}\quad \cancel{5}\quad {}^{1}4 \\
-\quad 1\quad 6\quad 7 \\
\hline
1\quad 8\quad 7
\end{array}
$$

2.

$$
\begin{array}{r}
3\quad {}^{1}1 \\
\cancel{4}\quad \cancel{2}\quad {}^{1}4 \\
-\quad 1\quad 7\quad 6 \\
\hline
2\quad 4\quad 7
\end{array}
$$

3.

$$
\begin{array}{r}
4\quad {}^{1}1 \\
\cancel{5}\quad \cancel{2}\quad {}^{1}4 \\
-\quad 1\quad 7\quad 8 \\
\hline
3\quad 4\quad 6
\end{array}
$$

4.

$$
\begin{array}{r}
2\quad {}^{1}1 \\
\cancel{3}\quad \cancel{2}\quad {}^{1}5 \\
-\quad 1\quad 5\quad 8 \\
\hline
1\quad 6\quad 7
\end{array}
$$

5.

$$
\begin{array}{r}
3\quad {}^{1}4 \\
\cancel{4}\quad \cancel{3}\quad {}^{1}6 \\
-\quad 1\quad 8\quad 7 \\
\hline
2\quad 4\quad 9
\end{array}
$$

6.

$$
\begin{array}{r}
2\quad {}^{1}3 \\
\cancel{3}\quad \cancel{4}\quad {}^{1}1 \\
-\quad 1\quad 7\quad 4 \\
\hline
1\quad 6\quad 7
\end{array}
$$

7. Correct

8. Miscalculated 14 − 9, should be:

$$
\begin{array}{r}
2\ \ \overset{7}{\cancel{8}}\ \ {}^{1}4 \\
-\ \ 1\ \ 3\ \ 9 \\
\hline
1\ \ 4\ \ 5
\end{array}
$$

9. No need to exchange for 6 − 3, should be:

$$
\begin{array}{r}
\overset{3}{\cancel{4}}\ \ {}^{1}1\ \ 6 \\
-\ \ 1\ \ 8\ \ 3 \\
\hline
2\ \ 3\ \ 3
\end{array}
$$

10. Correct

11. Need to exchange for 20 − 80, should be:

$$
\begin{array}{r}
\overset{4}{\cancel{5}}\ \ {}^{1}2\ \ 4 \\
-\ \ 1\ \ 8\ \ 3 \\
\hline
3\ \ 4\ \ 1
\end{array}
$$

12. Correct

Owl Largest answer:
875 − 134 = 741
Smallest answer:
513 − 487 = 26
Closest to 100:
481 − 375 = 106
475 − 381 = 94
841 − 735 = 106
835 − 741 = 94

Block B3

Page 19
Subtracting

1. 383 ⌄ 390 ⌄ 400
      7   10
400 − 383 = 17 cm

2. 464 ⌄ 470 ⌄ 500
      6   30
500 − 464 = 36 cm

3. 279 ⌄ 280 ⌄ 300
      1   20
300 − 279 = 21 cm

4. 542 ⌄ 550 ⌄ 600
      8   50
600 − 542 = 58 cm

5. 376 ⌄ 380 ⌄ 400
      4   20
400 − 376 = 24 cm

Owl Answers will vary.

6. 4997 + 3 = 5000
7. 3996 + 4 = 4000
8. 1989 + 11 = 2000
9. 984 + 6 = 1000
10. 2991 + 9 = 3000
11. 3995 + 5 = 4000
12. 4975 + 25 = 5000
13. 3955 + 45 = 4000
14. 6897 + 103 = 7000

Page 20
Subtracting

1. 4003 − 3996 = 7
2. 4009 − 3991 = 18
3. 7006 − 6997 = 9
4. 7005 − 6994 = 11
5. 7008 − 6993 = 15
6. 7011 − 6994 = 17

Owl There are 9: from
1001 − 991 = 10 to 1009 − 999 = 10

7. Any six from:
6043 − 5985 = 58 miles
6043 − 5025 = 1018 miles
6043 − 4998 = 1045 miles
6043 − 3970 = 2073 miles
5985 − 5025 = 960 miles
5985 − 4998 = 987 miles
5985 − 3970 = 2015 miles
5025 − 4998 = 27 miles
5025 − 3970 = 1055 miles
4998 − 3970 = 1028 miles

Page 21
Subtracting

1. 5014 − 4973 = 41
2. 3028 − 2947 = 81

3. $4017 - 3987 = 30$
4. $5020 - 4991 = 29$
5. $3051 - 2996 = 55$
6. $2079 - 1981 = 98$

Owl 1. £10·25
2. £20·25
3. £7·50
4. £7·25
5. £13·75
6. £24·50
7. 108 staples
8. £92
9. 61 miles

Page 22
Subtracting

1. £1046 – £989 = £57
2. £5054 – £4973 = £81
3. £3024 – £2994 = £30
4. £4069 – £3876 = £193
5. £2055 – £1988 = £67
6. £4078 – £3942 = £136
7. £1098 – £976 = £122
8. £6038 – £5984 = £54
9. £4036 – £3828 = £208
10. £5095 – £4865 = £230
11. £3069 – £2876 = £193
12. £2067 – £1978 = £89

Explore

Beth has 492 notes;
Juan has 508 notes

Page 23
Nines

1. $4 \times 9 = 36$
2. $5 \times 9 = 45$
3. $9 \times 9 = 81$
4. $3 \times 9 = 27$
5. $8 \times 9 = 72$
6. $7 \times 9 = 63$
7. $10 \times 9 = 90$

8. $2 \times 9 = 18$
9. $6 \times 9 = 54$
10. $45 \div 9 = 5$
11. $63 \div 9 = 7$
12. $27 \div 9 = 3$
13. $81 \div 9 = 9$

Owl 0, 1, 2, 3, 4, 5, 6, 7, 8, 9
9, 8, 7, 6, 5, 4, 3, 2, 1, 0
They are the numbers of the x9 table.

Page 24
Nines

1. $4 \times 9 = 36$
2. $6 \times 9 = 54$
3. $3 \times 9 = 27$
4. $1 \times 9 = 9$
5. $5 \times 9 = 45$
6. $7 \times 9 = 63$
7. $9 \times 9 = 81$
8. $2 \times 9 = 18$
9. $8 \times 9 = 72$
10. $1 \times 9 = 9$
11. $6 \times 9 = 54$
12. $45 \div 9 = 5$
13. $3 \times 9 = 27$
14. $5 \times 9 = 45$
15. $54 \div 9 = 6$
16. $4 \times 9 = 36$
17. $63 \div 9 = 7$
18. $9 \times 9 = 81$

Page 25
Nines

1. $2 \times 9 = 18$
2. $3 \times 9 = 27$
3. $72 \div 9 = 8$
4. $90 \div 9 = 10$
5. $4 \times 9 = 36$
6. $9 \times 1 = 9$
7. $81 \div 9 = 9$
8. $45 \div 5 = 9$
9. $8 \times 9 = 72$
10. $54 \div 6 = 9$

11.	$7 \times 9 = 63$		East and West
12.	$36 \div 4 = 9$		North-east and
13.	True		South-west
14.	False		North-west and South-east
15.	False	9.	Riptide
16.	False	10.	Surf Central
17.	False	11.	Deluge
18.	False	12.	Super Slide
Owl	Answers will vary.	13.	Surf Central
		14.	Rapids

Page 26
Nines

1. a: 18
   b: 72
2. c: 36
   d: 63
3. e: 90
   f: 540
4. g: 270
   h: 810
5. 81p
6. 8 dresses
7. 10 days, with 4 cans left over

Explore

Answers will vary.
Examples might include:
504, 513, 522, 531, 540;
603, 612, 621, 630;
702, 711, 720;
801, 810; 900
1008, 2754, 8361...

Page 27
Direction

1. North
2. East
3. West
4. South
5. North-east
6. South-east
7. North-west
8. South-west

Owl North and South

Page 28
Direction

1. Tokyo
2. Nagasaki
3. Akita
4. Matsue
5. Osaka
6. Matsue
7. Nagasaki
8. Tokyo
9. South-west
10. North-west
11. East

Page 29
Direction

1. South-east
2. North-east
3. East
4. North
5. North
6. South
7. North-east
8. West

Owl Answers will vary.

Page 30
Angles

1. 2 right angles
2. 3 right angles
3. 1 right angle

page 30 continued

4. 2 right angles
5. 2 right angles
6. 1 right angle
7. 1 right angle

Number of degrees:

1. 180°
2. 270°
3. 90°
4. 180°
5. 180°
6. 90°
7. 90°
8. 2 right angles
9. 2 right angles
10. 3 right angles
11. 1 right angle

Turning anti-clockwise:

8. 2 right angles
9. 2 right angles
10. 1 right angle
11. 3 right angles

Owl Answers will vary.

Page 31

Angles

1. South
2. South
3. North-east
4. North-west
5. North
6. South-east
7. 180°
8. 270°
9. 90°
10. 360°

Owl 8 times

Page 32

Angles

1. 90°
2. 225°

3. 135°
4. 45°
5. 315°
6. 90°
7. 135°
8. 90°
9. 45°

Owl 8 different changes of direction for a
90° turn:
North to East;
North-east to South-east;
East to South;
South-east to North-West;
South to West;
South-west to North-west;
West to North;
North-west to North-east;

10. 90° + 60° = 150°
11. 180°
12. 90° + 30° = 120°
13. 90°
14. 180° + 30° = 210°
15. 270° + 30° = 300°

Page 33

Angles

1. 90°
2. 180°
3. 60°
4. 150°
5. 150°
6. 60°
7. 300°
8. 120°
9. 30°
10. 240°

Explore

Hour hand:
8 right angles a day
Minute hand:
4 right angles an hour;
96 right angles a day

Block C3
Page 34
Weight
1. spider: grams
2. mouse: grams
3. ant: grams
4. beetle: grams
5. hamster: grams
6. dog: kilograms
7. cat: kilograms
8. $1\,kg = 1000\,g$
9. $\frac{1}{2}kg = 500\,g$
10. $\frac{1}{4}kg = 250\,g$
11. $1\frac{1}{2}kg = 1500\,g$
12. $\frac{3}{4}kg = 750\,g$
13. $1\frac{1}{4}kg = 1250\,g$
14. $2\,kg = 2000\,g$
15. $1\frac{3}{4}kg = 1750\,g$
16. $2\frac{1}{4}kg = 2250\,g$

Owl Answers will vary.

Page 35
Weight
1. mouse: 200 g
2. rabbit: 1 kg
3. cat: 8 kg
4. dog: 10 kg
5. hamster: 700 g
6. stick insect: 1 g

Owl Answers will vary.

7. $1250\,g = 1\frac{1}{4}$ kg
8. $1000\,g = 1\,kg$
9. $500\,g = \frac{1}{2}kg$
10. $2500\,g = 2\frac{1}{2}kg$
11. $2000\,g = 2\,kg$
12. $750\,g = \frac{3}{4}kg$
13. $1500\,g = 1\frac{1}{2}kg$
14. $2750\,g = 2\frac{3}{4}kg$

Page 36
Weight
1. 500 g
2. 500 g

3. 750 g
4. 1750 g
5. 600 g
6. 2250 g

Ten times each amount:
1. 5000 g or 5 kg
2. 5000 g or 5 kg
3. 7500 g or 7.5 kg
4. 17 500 g or 17.5 kg
5. 6000 g or 6 kg
6. 22 500 g or 22.5 kg
7. True
8. True
9. False
10. False
11. True
12. False

Owl Answers will vary.

Page 37
Weight
1. c: $\frac{1}{4}kg$
2. d: 300 g
3. b: 400 g
4. a: 800 g
5. f: $\frac{3}{4}kg$
6. e: 900 g

Owl a: £2
b: £1
c: 75p
d: 75p
e: £2·25
f: £2

7. 29 kg 700 g
8. 300 g
9. 300 g; 100 g

Page 38
Co-ordinates
1. football (b, 1)
2. chair (c, 1)

3. bookshelves (e, 2)
4. bike (d, 5)
5. sand tray (b, 4)
6. bricks (e, 4)
7. water tray (c, 3)
8. toy box (b, 2)
9. paints (e, 1)
Owl Answers will vary.

Page 39
Co-ordinates

1. trees
2. car
3. ice cream van
4. ducks
5. picnic bench
6. slide
7. tent
8. roundabout
9. bench
Owl Answers will vary.

Page 40
Co-ordinates

Inverness (4, 9)
Dundee (5, 8)
Edinburgh (5, 7)
Glasgow (4, 7)
Newcastle (6, 6)
Lancaster (5, 5)
York (6, 5)
Hull (7, 5)
Nottingham (6, 4)
Aberystwyth (4, 3)
Birmingham (6, 3)
London (7, 2)
Dover (8, 2)
Bristol (5, 2)
Plymouth (4, 1)
Owl York, Hull, Nottingham, Aberystwyth, Birmingham, London, Dover, Bristol, Plymouth

Page 41
Co-ordinates

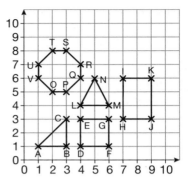

1. ABC: triangle
2. DEFG: square
3. HIJK: rectangle
4. LMN: triangle
5. OPQRSTUV: octagon
Explore Co-ordinates that add to 10

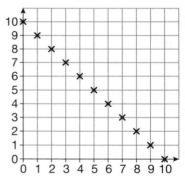

Co-ordinates that add to 6:

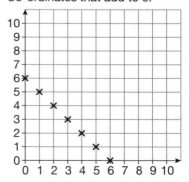

Page 42
Calendars

1. January, February, March, April,
   May, June, July, August, September,
   October, November, December
2. April, June, September, November
3. 7 months
4. 2008/ 2012

Owl Answers will vary.

Page 43
Calendars

1. Winter:
   December, January, February
   Spring:
   March, April, May
   Summer:
   June, July, August
   Autumn:
   September, October, November
2. 1st June
3. 7th June
4. 8th June
5. 4th June
6. 12th June
7. 10th June

Owl Answers will vary.

Page 44
Calendars

1. 5
2. Mondays
3. Wednesday 3rd
4. 4 days
5. Twice, 6th and 14th
6. 2 days
7. Friday 12th

Owl Answers will vary.

Page 45
Calendars

1. Exactly one month old: Wednesday
   First Sunday: 9th June

2. New Year's Eve: Friday
   First Saturday:
   1st January
   1st February:
   Tuesday
3. Friday

Explore Answers will vary.

Page 46
Carroll diagrams

1. Crawly
2. No other words
3. Climbing
4. tent, I, think, time, you, went
5. Yellow box
6. Pink box
7. Green box
8. Blue box
9. Answers will vary.

Page 47
Carroll and Venn diagrams

1.

	50 or more	Not 50 or more
Digital total is 12 or more	75 84 97	39 48 49
Digital total is not 12 or more	62 65 50 81	17 20 40

2.

50 or more   digital total 12 or more

62   65   75   39
   50   84   48
      81   97   49

17   20   40

Carroll and Venn diagrams

	Has one syllable	Has ~~one syllable~~
~~Begins with a vowel~~	and on in old or	arranged objects
Begins with a vowel	rows my new like jam me sort them	columns pages ready waiting receiving stages jellies letting Carroll diagrams

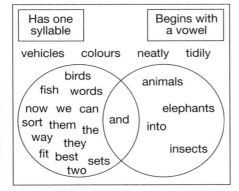

Owl Answers will vary.
An example might be:

	noun	not a noun
has one syllable		
does not have one syllable		

Adding money

Children should also include estimates.

1.
$$\begin{array}{r} £\,1\,6 \cdot 2\,7 \\ +\,£\,5 \cdot 5\,0 \\ \hline £\,2\,1 \cdot 7\,7 \\ 1 \end{array}$$

2.
$$\begin{array}{r} £\,8 \cdot 2\,5 \\ +\,£\,5 \cdot 5\,0 \\ \hline £\,1\,3 \cdot 7\,5 \end{array}$$

3.
$$\begin{array}{r} £\,4 \cdot 3\,5 \\ +\,£\,5 \cdot 5\,0 \\ \hline £\,9 \cdot 8\,5 \end{array}$$

4.
$$\begin{array}{r} £\,2\,5 \cdot 1\,9 \\ +\,£\,5 \cdot 5\,0 \\ \hline £\,3\,0 \cdot 6\,9 \\ 1 \end{array}$$

5.
$$\begin{array}{r} £\,1\,2 \cdot 4\,9 \\ +\,£\,5 \cdot 5\,0 \\ \hline £\,1\,7 \cdot 9\,9 \end{array}$$

6.
$$\begin{array}{r} £\,3\,2 \cdot 3\,5 \\ +\,£\,5 \cdot 5\,0 \\ \hline £\,3\,7 \cdot 8\,5 \end{array}$$

7.
$$\begin{array}{r} £\,2\,7 \cdot 2\,0 \\ +\,£\,5 \cdot 5\,0 \\ \hline £\,3\,2 \cdot 7\,0 \\ 1 \end{array}$$

Owl Pairs of tickets that can be bought after the £5·50 increase:
Exeter and Bristol
Exeter and Dublin
Pairs of tickets that can be bought before the increase:
Exeter and Bristol
Exeter and Dublin
Exeter and Amsterdam
Exeter and Paris

Bristol and Dublin

Bristol and Amsterdam

Amsterdam and Dublin

```
£   5 · 6 4
+ £   7 · 6 5
£ 1 3 · 2 9
      1
```

8.
```
£ 3 · 8 4
+ £ 2 · 7 5
£ 6 · 5 9
    1
```

```
£   5 · 6 4
+ £   8 · 9 3
£ 1 4 · 5 7
      1
```

9.
```
£ 4 · 7 5
+ £ 1 · 7 2
£ 6 · 4 7
    1
```

```
£   4 · 8 9
+ £   7 · 7 7
£ 1 2 · 6 6
      1   1
```

10.
```
£ 3 · 2 7
+ £ 2 · 3 8
£ 5 · 6 5
    1
```

```
£   4 · 8 9
+ £   6 · 5 8
£ 1 1 · 4 7
      1   1
```

11. £2·83 + £1·34 = £4·17

12. £5·25 + £2·37 = £7·62

13. £4·61 + £3·96 = £8·57

14. £6·34 + £1·57 = £7·91

15. £3·84 + £2·74 = £6·58

16. £5·66 + £2·52 = £8·18

```
£   4 · 8 9
+ £   7 · 6 5
£ 1 2 · 5 4
      1   1
```

Page 50

Adding money

Children should also include estimates.

1. Any six of:

```
£   5 · 6 4
+ £   4 · 8 9
£ 1 0 · 5 3
      1   1
```

```
£   4 · 8 9
+ £   8 · 9 3
£ 1 3 · 8 2
      1   1
```

```
£   5 · 6 4
+ £   7 · 7 7
£ 1 3 · 4 1
      1   1
```

```
£   7 · 7 7
+ £   6 · 5 8
£ 1 4 · 3 5
      1   1
```

```
£   5 · 6 4
+ £   6 · 5 8
£ 1 2 · 2 2
      1   1
```

```
£   7 · 7 7
+ £   7 · 6 5
£ 1 5 · 4 2
      1   1
```

```
£   7 · 7 7
+ £   8 · 9 3
£ 1 6 · 7 0
      1   1
```

Textbook 3

$$
\begin{array}{r}
£\quad 6\cdot 5\,8 \\
+\ £\quad 7\cdot 6\,5 \\
\hline
£\ 1\,4\cdot 2\,3 \\
{\scriptstyle 1\quad 1}
\end{array}
$$

$$
\begin{array}{r}
£\quad 6\cdot 5\,8 \\
+\ £\quad 8\cdot 9\,3 \\
\hline
£\ 1\,5\cdot 5\,1 \\
{\scriptstyle 1\quad 1}
\end{array}
$$

$$
\begin{array}{r}
£\quad 7\cdot 6\,5 \\
+\ £\quad 8\cdot 9\,3 \\
\hline
£\ 1\,6\cdot 5\,8 \\
{\scriptstyle 1}
\end{array}
$$

Owl
$$
\begin{array}{r}
£\quad 4\cdot 4\,6 \\
+\ £\quad 5\cdot 5\,4 \\
\hline
£\ 1\,0\cdot 0\,0 \\
{\scriptstyle 1\quad 1}
\end{array}
$$

2.
$$
\begin{array}{r}
£\quad 3\cdot 3\,2 \\
£\quad 4\cdot 5\,3 \\
+\ £\quad 3\cdot 4\,5 \\
\hline
£\ 1\,1\cdot 3\,0 \\
{\scriptstyle 1\quad 1}
\end{array}
$$

3.
$$
\begin{array}{r}
£\,4\cdot 3\,6 \\
£\,2\cdot 2\,7 \\
+\ £\,2\cdot 1\,5 \\
\hline
£\,8\cdot 7\,8 \\
{\scriptstyle 1}
\end{array}
$$

4.
$$
\begin{array}{r}
£\,2\cdot 8\,1 \\
£\,1\cdot 9\,1 \\
+\ £\,1\cdot 7\,3 \\
\hline
£\,6\cdot 4\,5 \\
{\scriptstyle 2}
\end{array}
$$

5.
$$
\begin{array}{r}
£\,3\cdot 2\,1 \\
£\,2\cdot 3\,2 \\
+\ £\,3\cdot 9\,7 \\
\hline
£\,9\cdot 5\,0 \\
{\scriptstyle 1\quad 1}
\end{array}
$$

6.
$$
\begin{array}{r}
£\,4\cdot 1\,4 \\
£\,3\cdot 6\,7 \\
+\ £\,2\cdot 1\,5 \\
\hline
£\,9\cdot 9\,6 \\
{\scriptstyle 1}
\end{array}
$$

7.
$$
\begin{array}{r}
£\,4\cdot 5\,3 \\
£\,2\cdot 6\,2 \\
+\ £\,1\cdot 4\,1 \\
\hline
£\,8\cdot 5\,6 \\
{\scriptstyle 1}
\end{array}
$$

Page 5I
Adding money

Children should also include estimates.

1.
$$
\begin{array}{r}
£\,2\cdot 7\,5 \\
+\ £\,3\cdot 8\,6 \\
\hline
£\,6\cdot 6\,1 \\
{\scriptstyle 1\quad 1}
\end{array}
$$

2.
$$
\begin{array}{r}
£\quad 3\cdot 6\,6 \\
+\ £\quad 7\cdot 7\,5 \\
\hline
£\ 1\,1\cdot 4\,1 \\
{\scriptstyle 1\quad 1}
\end{array}
$$

3.
$$
\begin{array}{r}
£\quad 4\cdot 8\,4 \\
+\ £\quad 8\cdot 9\,6 \\
\hline
£\ 1\,3\cdot 8\,0 \\
{\scriptstyle 1\quad 1}
\end{array}
$$

4.
$$
\begin{array}{r}
£\,3\cdot 4\,7 \\
+\ £\,2\cdot 8\,6 \\
\hline
£\,6\cdot 3\,3 \\
{\scriptstyle 1\quad 1}
\end{array}
$$

5.
$$
\begin{array}{r}
£\,4\cdot 5\,7 \\
+\ £\,1\cdot 6\,8 \\
\hline
£\,6\cdot 2\,5 \\
{\scriptstyle 1\quad 1}
\end{array}
$$

6.
$$
\begin{array}{r}
£\,2\cdot 7\,5 \\
+\ £\,2\cdot 4\,9 \\
\hline
£\,5\cdot 2\,4 \\
{\scriptstyle 1\quad 1}
\end{array}
$$

7.
$$
\begin{array}{r}
£\,5\cdot 4\,8 \\
+\ £\,1\cdot 7\,5 \\
\hline
£\,7\cdot 2\,3 \\
{\scriptstyle 1\quad 1}
\end{array}
$$

8.

```
   £ 4 · 8 7
 + £ 1 · 5 6
   £ 6 · 4 3
       1   1
```

```
   £ 7 · 7 5
   £ 6 · 7 7
 + £ 7 · 8 6
   £ 2 2 · 3 8
         2   1
```

9. Any six of:

```
   £ 7 · 7 5
   £ 5 · 6 9
 + £ 8 · 6 6
   £ 2 2 · 1 0
         2   2
```

```
   £ 7 · 7 5
   £ 8 · 9 4
 + £ 7 · 8 6
   £ 2 4 · 5 5
         2   1
```

```
   £ 7 · 7 5
   £ 5 · 6 9
 + £ 6 · 7 7
   £ 2 0 · 2 1
         2   2
```

```
   £ 5 · 6 9
   £ 8 · 6 6
 + £ 6 · 7 7
   £ 2 1 · 1 2
         2   2
```

```
   £ 7 · 7 5
   £ 5 · 6 9
 + £ 8 · 9 4
   £ 2 2 · 3 8
         2   1
```

```
   £ 5 · 6 9
   £ 8 · 6 6
 + £ 8 · 9 4
   £ 2 3 · 2 9
         2   1
```

```
   £ 7 · 7 5
   £ 5 · 6 9
 + £ 7 · 8 6
   £ 2 1 · 3 0
         2   2
```

```
   £ 5 · 6 9
   £ 8 · 6 6
 + £ 7 · 8 6
   £ 2 2 · 2 1
         2   2
```

```
   £ 7 · 7 5
   £ 8 · 6 6
 + £ 6 · 7 7
   £ 2 3 · 1 8
         2   1
```

```
   £ 5 · 6 9
   £ 6 · 7 7
 + £ 8 · 9 4
   £ 2 1 · 4 0
         2   2
```

```
   £ 7 · 7 5
   £ 8 · 6 6
 + £ 7 · 8 6
   £ 2 4 · 2 7
         2   1
```

```
   £ 5 · 6 9
   £ 6 · 7 7
 + £ 7 · 8 6
   £ 2 0 · 3 2
         2   2
```

```
   £ 7 · 7 5
   £ 6 · 7 7
 + £ 8 · 9 4
   £ 2 3 · 4 6
         2   1
```

```
   £ 8 · 6 6
   £ 6 · 7 7
 + £ 8 · 9 4
   £ 2 4 · 3 7
         2   1
```

$$
\begin{array}{r}
£\quad 8 \cdot 6\,6 \\
£\quad 6 \cdot 7\,7 \\
+\ £\quad 7 \cdot 8\,6 \\
\hline
£\ 2\,3 \cdot 2\,9 \\
2\quad 1
\end{array}
$$

$$
\begin{array}{r}
£\quad 6 \cdot 7\,7 \\
£\quad 8 \cdot 9\,4 \\
+\ £\quad 7 \cdot 8\,6 \\
\hline
£\ 2\,3 \cdot 5\,7 \\
2\quad 1
\end{array}
$$

Total cost of all the videos: £45·67
Owl Answers will vary.

Page 52
Adding money

1. £3·68 + £5·38 = £9·06
   £5·38 + £5·86 = £11·24
   £4·75 + 5·69 = £10·44
   £6·57 + £5·86 = £12·43
   £3·68 + £4·75 = £8·43
   £6·57 + £5·69 = £12·26
2. £22·87
3. £18·12
4. £34·84
5. £10·38
Owl Answers will vary.
   Possible answers include:
   £1·24 + £8·76
   £3·79 + £6·21
   £5·68 + £4·32

Page 53
Subtracting money

Children should also include estimates.

1. $$\begin{array}{r} £\ 7 \cdot 4\,0 \\ -\ £\ 1 \cdot 3\,0 \\ \hline £\ 6 \cdot 1\,0 \end{array}$$

2. $$\begin{array}{r} £\ 8 \cdot 4\,0 \\ -\ £\ 1 \cdot 3\,0 \\ \hline £\ 7 \cdot 1\,0 \end{array}$$

3. $$\begin{array}{r} £\ 9 \cdot 6\,0 \\ -\ £\ 1 \cdot 3\,0 \\ \hline £\ 8 \cdot 3\,0 \end{array}$$

4. $$\begin{array}{r} £\ 7 \cdot 7\,0 \\ -\ £\ 1 \cdot 3\,0 \\ \hline £\ 6 \cdot 4\,0 \end{array}$$

5. $$\begin{array}{r} £\ 8 \cdot 9\,0 \\ -\ £\ 1 \cdot 3\,0 \\ \hline £\ 7 \cdot 6\,0 \end{array}$$

6. $$\begin{array}{r} £\ 6 \cdot 8\,0 \\ -\ £\ 1 \cdot 3\,0 \\ \hline £\ 5 \cdot 5\,0 \end{array}$$

7. $$\begin{array}{r} £\ 5 \cdot 7\,0 \\ -\ £\ 1 \cdot 3\,0 \\ \hline £\ 4 \cdot 4\,0 \end{array}$$

Owl 6 times

8. $$\begin{array}{r} £\ 4 \cdot \overset{4}{\cancel{5}}\,{}^{1}2 \\ -\ £\ 2 \cdot 3\,6 \\ \hline £\ 2 \cdot 1\,6 \end{array}$$

9. $$\begin{array}{r} £\ 2 \cdot \overset{6}{\cancel{7}}\,{}^{1}3 \\ -\ £\ 1 \cdot 4\,8 \\ \hline £\ 1 \cdot 2\,5 \end{array}$$

10. £3·42 – £1·28 = £2·14
11. £4·66 – £2·48 = £2·18
12. £6·72 - £3·16 = £3·56
13. £5·53 - £3·27 = £2·26
14. £4·61 - £2·48 = £2·13
15. £5·88 - £4·69 = £1·19

Page 54
Subtracting money

Children should also include estimates.

1. $$\begin{array}{r} £\ \overset{7}{\cancel{8}} \cdot {}^{1}2\,6 \\ -\ £\ 4 \cdot 4\,2 \\ \hline £\ 3 \cdot 8\,4 \end{array}$$

Textbook 3

or

$$\begin{array}{r} \overset{7}{\cancel{0}} \cdot {}^{1}2\,6 \\[-2pt] \pounds\ \\ -\ \pounds\ 6 \cdot\ 6\ 1 \\ \hline \pounds\ 1 \cdot\ 6\ 5 \\ \hline \end{array}$$

£ $\overset{7}{\cancel{0}}$ · ¹2 6
− £ 6 · 6 1
£ 1 · 6 5

or

£ $\overset{7}{\cancel{0}}$ · ¹2 6
− £ 5 · 5 3
£ 2 · 7 3

or

£ $\overset{7}{\cancel{0}}$ · ¹2 6
− £ 3 · 8 4
£ 4 · 4 2

2.
£ $\overset{8}{\cancel{9}}$ · ¹1 8
− £ 4 · 4 2
£ 4 · 7 6

or

£ $\overset{8}{\cancel{9}}$ · ¹1 8
− £ 6 · 6 1
£ 2 · 5 7

or

£ $\overset{8}{\cancel{9}}$ · ¹1 8
− £ 5 · 5 3
£ 3 · 6 5

or

£ $\overset{8}{\cancel{9}}$ · ¹1 8
− £ 3 · 8 4
£ 5 · 3 4

3.
£ $\overset{9}{\cancel{1}}$ 1$\overset{}{\cancel{0}}$ · ¹2 6
− £ 4 · 4 2
£ 5 · 8 4

or

£ $\overset{9}{\cancel{1}}$ 1$\overset{}{\cancel{0}}$ · ¹2 6
− £ 6 · 6 1
£ 3 · 6 5

or

£ $\overset{9}{\cancel{1}}$ 1$\overset{}{\cancel{0}}$ · ¹2 6
− £ 5 · 5 3
£ 4 · 7 3

or

£ $\overset{9}{\cancel{1}}$ 1$\overset{}{\cancel{0}}$ · ¹2 6
− £ 3 · 8 4
£ 6 · 4 2

4.
£ $\overset{4}{\cancel{5}}$ · ¹2 8
− £ 4 · 4 2
£ 0 · 8 6

or

£ $\overset{4}{\cancel{5}}$ · ¹2 8
− £ 3 · 8 4
£ 1 · 4 4

5.
£ $\overset{9}{\cancel{1}}$ 1$\overset{}{\cancel{0}}$ · ¹3 8
− £ 4 · 4 2
£ 5 · 9 6

or

£ $\overset{9}{\cancel{1}}$ 1$\overset{}{\cancel{0}}$ · ¹3 8
− £ 6 · 6 1
£ 3 · 7 7

or

£ $\overset{9}{\cancel{1}}$ 1$\overset{}{\cancel{0}}$ · ¹3 8
− £ 5 · 5 3
£ 4 · 8 5

or

£ $\overset{9}{\cancel{1}}$ 1$\overset{}{\cancel{0}}$ · ¹3 8
− £ 3 · 8 4
£ 6 · 5 4

6.
```
        8
    £ 9̸ · ¹2 9
  – £ 4 ·  4 2
    £ 4 ·  8 7
```

or

```
        8
    £ 9̸ · ¹2 9
  – £ 6 ·  6 1
    £ 2 ·  6 8
```

or

```
        8
    £ 9̸ · ¹2 9
  – £ 5 ·  5 3
    £ 3 ·  7 6
```

or

```
        8
    £ 9̸ · ¹2 9
  – £ 3 ·  8 4
    £ 5 ·  4 5
```

7.
```
        6
    £ 7̸ · ¹3 6
  – £ 4 ·  4 2
    £ 2 ·  9 4
```

or

```
        6
    £ 7̸ · ¹3 6
  – £ 6 ·  6 1
    £ 0 ·  7 5
```

or

```
        6
    £ 7̸ · ¹3 6
  – £ 5 ·  5 3
    £ 1 ·  8 3
```

or

```
        6
    £ 7̸ · ¹3 6
  – £ 3 ·  8 4
    £ 3 ·  5 2
```

8.
```
        7
    £ 8̸ · ¹2 8
  – £ 4 ·  4 2
    £ 3 ·  8 6
```

or

```
        7
    £ 8̸ · ¹2 8
  – £ 6 ·  6 1
    £ 1 ·  6 7
```

or

```
        7
    £ 8̸ · ¹2 8
  – £ 5 ·  5 3
    £ 2 ·  7 5
```

or

```
        7
    £ 8̸ · ¹2 8
  – £ 3 ·  8 4
    £ 4 ·  4 4
```

9.
```
          9
    £ 1̸ ¹0̸ · ¹1 7
  – £    4 ·  4 2
    £    5 ·  7 5
```

or

```
          9
    £ 1̸ ¹0̸ · ¹1 7
  – £    6 ·  6 1
    £    3 ·  5 6
```

or

```
          9
    £ 1̸ ¹0̸ · ¹1 7
  – £    5 ·  5 3
    £    4 ·  6 4
```

or

```
          9
    £ 1̸ ¹0̸ · ¹1 7
  – £    3 ·  8 4
    £    6 ·  3 3
```

10. $\begin{array}{r} \overset{3}{\cancel{4}} \cdot {}^{1}1\,9 \\ -\ £\,3\,\cdot\,2\,6 \\ \hline £\,0\,\cdot\,9\,3 \end{array}$ (£ 4·119 − £3·26 = £0·93)

11. £ $\overset{7}{\cancel{8}}$ · ${}^{1}2$ 6
 − £ 4 · 7 5
 £ 3 · 5 1

12. £ $\overset{3}{\cancel{4}}$ · ${}^{1}5$ 7
 − £ 2 · 8 6
 £ 1 · 7 1

13. £ $\overset{4}{\cancel{5}}$ · ${}^{1}4$ 8
 − £ 2 · 7 5
 £ 2 · 7 3

14. £ 6 · $\overset{8}{\cancel{9}}$ 14
 − £ 1 · 2 6
 £ 5 · 6 8

15. £ 5 · $\overset{7}{\cancel{8}}$ ${}^{1}6$
 − £ 3 · 4 7
 £ 2 · 3 9

16. £ $\overset{3}{\cancel{4}}$ · ${}^{1}3$ 8
 − £ 1 · 6 4
 £ 2 · 7 4

17. £ 7 · $\overset{6}{\cancel{7}}$ 12
 − £ 2 · 1 9
 £ 5 · 5 3

Owl Answers will vary.

Page 55
Subtracting money

Children should also include estimates.

1. £ $\overset{1}{\cancel{2}}$ · $\overset{13}{\cancel{4}}$ 18
 − £ 1 · 6 9
 £ 0 · 7 9

2. £ $\overset{2}{\cancel{3}}$ · $\overset{10}{\cancel{1}}$ 12
 − £ 1 · 8 7
 £ 1 · 2 5

3. £ $\overset{2}{\cancel{3}}$ · $\overset{11}{\cancel{2}}$ 14
 − £ 1 · 7 6
 £ 1 · 4 8

4. £ $\overset{4}{\cancel{5}}$ · $\overset{10}{\cancel{1}}$ 16
 − £ 2 · 8 7
 £ 2 · 2 9

5. £ $\overset{1}{\cancel{2}}$ · $\overset{13}{\cancel{4}}$ 13
 − £ 1 · 9 5
 £ 0 · 4 8

6. £ $\overset{1}{\cancel{2}}$ · $\overset{15}{\cancel{0}}$ 15
 − £ 2 · 3 2
 £ 0 · 3 3

7. 95p

8. £1·51

9. £15·07

10. £3·23 − £1·88 = £1·35

11. £14·14 − £9·85 = £4·29

12. £9·23 − £5·76 = £3·47

13. £12·40 − £4·97 = £7·43

14. £8·12 − £4·86 = £3·26

15. £5·21 − £3·75 = £1·46

Owl £9·71 − £3·28 = £6·43

Page 56
Subtracting money

1. Correct

2. Correct

3. Correct

4. $\begin{array}{r} \overset{8}{}\ \ \\ 8 \cdot \overset{8}{\cancel{9}}\,11 \\ -\ 1 \cdot 0\,8 \\ \hline 7 \cdot 8\,3 \end{array}$

5. Correct
6. Correct
7. Correct

8.
$$
\begin{array}{r}
1\ 5\ \cdot\ \overset{6}{\cancel{7}}\,{}^{1}1 \\
-\quad 9\ \cdot\ 0\ 8 \\
\hline
6\ \cdot\ 6\ 3
\end{array}
$$

9. Correct

Explore The difference between the sum and difference of the two numbers is equal to double the smaller number.

Page 57

Sevens

1. $4 \times 7 = 28$ days
2. $5 \times 7 = 35$ days
3. $7 \times 7 = 49$ days
4. $3 \times 7 = 21$ days
5. $6 \times 7 = 42$ days
6. $2 \times 7 = 14$ days
7. $9 \times 7 = 63$ days
8. $8 \times 7 = 56$ days
9. $11 \times 7 = 77$ days
Owl $42 \times 7 = 294$ days
10. $5 \times 7 = 35$
11. $10 \times 7 = 70$
12. $2 \times 7 = 14$
13. $7 \times 7 = 49$
14. $3 \times 7 = 21$
15. $6 \times 7 = 42$
16. $4 \times 7 = 28$
17. $9 \times 7 = 63$
18. $11 \times 7 = 77$
19. $8 \times 7 = 56$
20. $0 \times 7 = 0$
21. $20 \times 7 = 140$

Page 58

Sevens

1. $35 \div 7 = 5$ weeks
2. $21 \div 7 = 3$ weeks
3. $56 \div 7 = 8$ weeks
4. $14 \div 7 = 2$ weeks
5. $63 \div 7 = 9$ weeks
6. $49 \div 7 = 7$ weeks
7. $28 \div 7 = 4$ weeks
8. $42 \div 7 = 6$ weeks
9. $77 \div 7 = 11$ weeks
Owl Answers will vary.
10. $21 \div 7 = 3$
11. $70 \div 7 = 10$
12. $14 \div 7 = 2$
13. $28 \div 7 = 4$
14. $49 \div 7 = 7$
15. $42 \div 7 = 6$
16. $7 \div 7 = 1$
17. $35 \div 7 = 5$
18. $77 \div 7 = 11$
19. $63 \div 7 = 9$
20. $56 \div 7 = 8$
21. $700 \div 7 = 100$

Page 59

Sevens

1. $2 \times 7 = 14$
2. $5 \times 7 = 35$
3. $7 \times 7 = 49$
4. $20 \times 7 = 140$
5. $8 \times 7 = 56$
6. $6 \times 7 = 42$
7. $10 \times 7 = 70$
8. $3 \times 7 = 21$
9. $9 \times 7 = 63$
Owl $31 \times 7 = 217$ sweets
10. 4 bags
11. 9 bags
12. 11 bags
13. 20 bags
14. 26 bags
15. 260 bags

Page 60

Sevens

1–4.

2s	2	4	6	8	10	12	14	16	18	20
5s	5	10	15	20	25	30	35	40	45	50
7s	7	14	21	28	35	42	49	56	63	70
10s	10	20	30	40	50	60	70	80	90	100

Owl ×14 table:
14, 28, 42, 56, 70, 84, 98, 112, 126, 140

5. 35
6. 28
7. 21 or 42 or 63
8. $3 \times 7 = 21$
9. $14 \div 7 = 2$
10. $6 \times 7 = 42$
11. $21 \div 7 = 3$
12. $28 \div 7 = 4$
13. $9 \times 7 = 63$
14. $7 \times 7 = 49$
15. $42 \div 7 = 6$
16. $35 \div 7 = 5$
17. $8 \times 7 = 56$
18. $5 \times 7 = 35$
19. $56 \div 7 = 8$

Page 6I

Multiplying

1. $4 \times 20 = 80\,cm$
2. $5 \times 30 = 150\,cm$
3. $6 \times 40 = 240\,cm$
4. $3 \times 60 = 180\,cm$
5. $8 \times 50 = 400\,cm$
6. $3 \times 30 = 90\,cm$
7. $6 \times 60 = 360\,cm$
8. $4 \times 80 = 320\,cm$
9. $5 \times 50 = 250\,cm$
Owl Triangle: 160 cm
Square: 120 cm
Pentagon: 96 cm
Hexagon: 80 cm
Octagon: 60 cm
Decagon: 48 cm
Dodecagon: 40 cm
10. $5 \times 50 = 250\,cm$
11. $6 \times 30 = 180\,cm$
12. $4 \times 60 = 240\,cm$
13. $3 \times 40 = 120\,cm$
14. $8 \times 60 = 480\,cm$
15. $7 \times 70 = 490\,cm$

Page 62

Multiplying

1. $3 \times 43 = (3 \times 40) + (3 \times 3)$
$= 120 + 9 = 129$
2. $4 \times 36 = (4 \times 30) + (4 \times 6)$
$= 120 + 24 = 144$
3. $5 \times 27 = (5 \times 20) + (5 \times 7)$
$= 100 + 35 = 135$
4. $9 \times 17 = (9 \times 10) + (9 \times 7)$
$= 90 + 63 = 153$
5. $7 \times 52 = (7 \times 50) + (7 \times 2)$
$= 350 + 14 = 364$
6. $6 \times 24 = (6 \times 20) + (6 \times 4)$
$= 120 + 24 = 144$
7. $8 \times 32 = (8 \times 30) + (8 \times 2)$
$= 240 + 16 = 256$
8. $3 \times 32 = (3 \times 30) + (3 \times 2)$
$= 90 + 6 = 96p$
9. $4 \times 28 = (4 \times 20) + (4 \times 8)$
$= 80 + 32 = £1·12$
10. $6 \times 57 = (6 \times 50) + (6 \times 7)$
$= 300 + 42 = £3·42$
11. $5 \times 42 = (5 \times 40) + (5 \times 2)$
$= 200 + 10 = £2·10$
12. $7 \times 46 = (7 \times 40) + (7 \times 6)$
$= 280 + 42 = £3·22$
13. $8 \times 35 = (8 \times 30) + (8 \times 5)$
$= 240 + 40 = £2·80$
14. $3 \times 28 = (3 \times 20) + (3 \times 8)$
$= 60 + 24 = 84p$
$4 \times 32 = (4 \times 30) + (4 \times 2)$
$= 120 + 8 = £1·28$
$84p + £1·28 = £2·12$

15. $4 \times 57 = (4 \times 50) + (4 \times 7)$
$\qquad = 200 + 28 = £2·28$
$3 \times 46 = (3 \times 40) + (3 \times 6)$
$\qquad = 120 + 18 = £1·38$
£2.28 + £1·38 = £3·66

Owl Answers will vary.
Lowest possible cost:
$4 \times 28 = £1·12$;
Highest possible cost:
$4 \times 57 = £2·28$

Page 63
Multiplying

1.

	30	7
5	150	35

$5 \times 37 = 185$

$$\begin{array}{r} 1\ 5\ 0 \\ +\quad 3\ 5 \\ \hline 1\ 8\ 5 \end{array}$$

2.

	40	3
6	240	18

$6 \times 43 = 258$

$$\begin{array}{r} 2\ 4\ 0 \\ +\quad 1\ 8 \\ \hline 2\ 5\ 8 \end{array}$$

3.

	20	8
3	60	24

$3 \times 28 = 84$

$$\begin{array}{r} 6\ 0 \\ +\ 2\ 4 \\ \hline 8\ 4 \end{array}$$

4.

	70	2
4	280	8

$4 \times 72 = 288$

$$\begin{array}{r} 2\ 8\ 0 \\ +\qquad 8 \\ \hline 2\ 8\ 8 \end{array}$$

5.

	30	4
8	240	32

$8 \times 34 = 272$

$$\begin{array}{r} 2\ 4\ 0 \\ +\quad 3\ 2 \\ \hline 2\ 7\ 2 \end{array}$$

6.

	40	2
9	360	18

$9 \times 42 = 378$

$$\begin{array}{r} 3\ 6\ 0 \\ +\quad 1\ 8 \\ \hline 3\ 7\ 8 \end{array}$$

7. estimate: $3 \times 30 = 90$

	20	7
3	60	21

$3 \times 27 = 81$

8. estimate: $4 \times 40 = 160$

	40	3
4	160	12

$4 \times 43 = 172$

9. estimate: $5 \times 40 = 200$

	30	8
5	150	40

$5 \times 38 = 190$

10. estimate: $6 \times 70 = 420$

	70	4
6	420	24

$6 \times 74 = 444$

11. estimate: $7 \times 30 = 210$

	30	3
7	210	21

$7 \times 33 = 231$

12. estimate: $8 \times 30 = 240$

	20	9
8	160	72

$8 \times 29 = 232$

Owl Answers will vary.
Possible answers include:
$9 \times 26 = 234$
$8 \times 29 = 232$
$7 \times 34 = 238$
$6 \times 39 = 234$
$5 \times 47 = 235$
$4 \times 59 = 236$
$3 \times 79 = 237$

Page 64
Multiplying

1. £3·12
2. £2·40 per week,
55p cheaper with travel pass
3. £190
4. $5 \times 43 = 215$
5. $7 \times 26 = 182$
6. $6 \times 48 = 288$

7. $5 \times 28 = 140$
8. $4 \times 37 = 148$
9. $8 \times 79 = 632$
Owl Answers will vary.
Possible examples lie between:
$23 \times 5 = 115$
$33 \times 9 = 297$

Block E3

Page 65

Multiplying

Children should also include estimates.

1.
```
    2 3
 ×    4
    8 0    4 × 2 0
    1 2    4 × 3
    9 2
```

2.
```
    4 2
 ×    7
  2 8 0    7 × 4 0
    1 4    7 × 2
  2 9 4
```

3.
```
    3 8
 ×    3
    9 0    3 × 3 0
    2 4    3 × 8
  1 1 4
```

4.
```
    8 2
 ×    6
  4 8 0    6 × 8 0
    1 2    6 × 2
  4 9 2
```

5.
```
    2 8
 ×    5
  1 0 0    5 × 2 0
    4 0    5 × 8
  1 4 0
```

6.
```
      5 6
 ×      4
  2 0 0    4 × 5 0
    2 4    4 × 6
  2 2 4
```

7.
```
      6 3
 ×      6
  3 6 0    6 × 6 0
    1 8    6 × 3
  3 7 8
```

8. $16 \times 5 = 80$ days
9. $23 \times 5 = 115$ days
10. $35 \times 5 = 175$ days
11. $43 \times 5 = 215$ days
12. $19 \times 5 = 95$ days
13. $28 \times 5 = 140$ days
Owl Answers will vary.

Page 66

Multiplying

Children should also include estimates.

1.
```
      2 6
 ×      6
  1 2 0
    3 6
  1 5 6 p
  = £1·56
```

2.
```
    2 4
 ×    3
    6 0
    1 2
    7 2 p
  = 72p
```

3.
```
    1 8
 ×    9
    9 0
    7 2
  1 6 2 p
  = £1·62
```

4.
```
    3 7
×     4
  1 2 0
    2 8
  1 4 8 p
```
= £1·48

5.
```
    3 4
×     5
  1 5 0
    2 0
  1 7 0 p
```
= £1·70

6.
```
    1 4
×     7
    7 0
    2 8
    9 8 p
```
= 98p

8-minute calls:

1.
```
    2 6
×     8
  1 6 0
    4 8
  2 0 8 p
```
= £2·08

2.
```
    2 4
×     8
  1 6 0
    3 2
  1 9 2 p
```
= £1·92

3.
```
    1 8
×     8
    8 0
    6 4
  1 4 4 p
```
= £1·44

4.
```
    3 7
×     8
  2 4 0
    5 6
  2 9 6 p
```
= £2·96

5.
```
    3 4
×     8
  2 4 0
    3 2
  2 7 2 p
```
= £2·72

6.
```
    1 4
×     8
    8 0
    3 2
  1 1 2 p
```
= £1·12

Owl Shelley: 7 minutes, 18p left
Simon: 14 minutes, 4p left
Azize: 5 minutes, 30p left
Lizzie: 11 minutes, 2p left
Sangeet: 8 minutes, 8p left
Zoe: 5 minutes, 15p left

7. 8 children

8. 276 buns

Page 67
Multiplying

Children should also include estimates.

1.
```
    2 4
×     7
  1 4 0
    2 8
  1 6 8
```

2.
```
    4 3
×     8
  3 2 0
    2 4
  3 4 4
```

3.
```
      2 7
 ×      5
  1 0 0
      3 5
  1 3 5
```

4.
```
      3 6
 ×      6
  1 8 0
      3 6
  2 1 6
  1
```

5.
```
      8 4
 ×      3
  2 4 0
      1 2
  2 5 2
```

6.
```
      2 8
 ×      9
  1 8 0
      7 2
  2 5 2
  1
```

7.
```
      7 2
 ×      4
  2 8 0
        8
  2 8 8
```

8.
```
      8 5
 ×      7
  5 6 0
      3 5
  5 9 5
```

9.
```
      4 8
 ×      3
  1 2 0
      2 4
  1 4 4
```

10. $6 \times 48p = £2·88$
11. $4 \times 27p = £1·08$

12. $7 \times 32p = £2·24$
13. $5 \times 63p = £3·15$
14. $8 \times 18p = £1·44$
15. $4 \times 17p = 68p$
Owl Answers will vary.

Page 68
Multiplying

Children should also include estimates.

1.
```
      8 6
 ×      6
  4 8 0
      3 6
  5 1 6
  1
  = £516
```

2.
```
      3 2
 ×      3
    9 0
      6
    9 6
  = £96
```

3.
```
      4 7
 ×      4
  1 6 0
      2 8
  1 8 8
  = £188
```

4.
```
      4 3
 ×      2
    8 0
      6
    8 6
  = £86
```

5.
```
      5 8
 ×      6
  3 0 0
      4 8
  3 4 8
  = £348
```

Textbook 3

6.
```
      6 3
×       3
  1 8 0
      9
  1 8 9
= £189
```

7.
```
      7 4
×       7
  4 9 0
    2 8
  5 1 8
  1
= £518
```

8.
```
      2 8
×       4
    8 0
    3 2
  1 1 2
= £112
```

9.
```
      2 4
×       2
    4 0
      8
    4 8
= £48
```

Explore

Largest answers:

$54 \times 6 = 324$

$87 \times 9 = 783$

Smallest answers:

$45 \times 3 = 135$

$78 \times 6 = 468$

Page 69

Dividing

1.
```
      1 2
  4|4 8
    4 0      10 × 4
      8       2 × 4
      0
```

2.
```
      1 3
  6|7 8
    6 0      10 × 6
    1 8       3 × 6
      0
```

3.
```
      1 7
  5|8 5
    5 0      10 × 5
    3 5       7 × 5
      0
```

4.
```
      1 7
  3|5 1
    3 0      10 × 3
    2 1       7 × 3
      0
```

5.
```
      1 2
  8|9 6
    8 0      10 × 8
    1 6       2 × 8
      0
```

6.
```
  3|4 8
  1 6 days
```

7.
```
  3|5 4
  1 8 days
```

8.
```
  3|5 7
  1 9 days
```

Owl 6. 12 days

7. 13 days, with 2 left or $13\frac{1}{2}$ days

8. 14 days, with 1 left or $14\frac{1}{4}$ days

Page 70

Dividing

1.
```
      1 8
  4|7 2
    4 0      10 × 4
    3 2       8 × 4
      0
  18 days
```

2.
```
    1 7
 3 ⟌5 1
    3 0   1 0 × 3
    2 1     7 × 3
      0
```
17 days

3.
```
    1 5
 5 ⟌7 5
    5 0   1 0 × 5
    2 5     5 × 5
      0
```
15 days

4.
```
    1 4
 6 ⟌8 4
    6 0   1 0 × 6
    2 4     4 × 6
      0
```
14 days

5.
```
    2 4
 4 ⟌9 6
    8 0   2 0 × 4
    1 6     4 × 4
      0
```
24 days

6.
```
    2 8
 3 ⟌8 4
    6 0   2 0 × 3
    2 4     8 × 3
      0
```
28 days

Owl 72+51+75+84+96+84 = 462 pages. 10 pages a day = 46·2 days or rounded up 47 days.

7.
```
    1 5
 3 ⟌4 5
```

8.
```
    1 9
 5 ⟌9 5
```

9.
```
    1 8
 3 ⟌5 4
```

10.
```
    1 9
 4 ⟌7 6
```

11.
```
    1 2
 6 ⟌7 2
```

12.
```
    1 3
 5 ⟌6 5
```

13.
```
    1 7
 4 ⟌6 8
```

14.
```
    1 2
 7 ⟌8 4
```

15.
```
    2 5
 3 ⟌7 5
```

Page 71

Dividing

1.
```
 4 ⟌7 6
    4 0   1 0 × 4
    3 6     9 × 4
      0
```
£19 each

2.
```
 3 ⟌5 1
    3 0   1 0 × 3
    2 1     7 × 3
      0
```
£17 each

3.
```
 5 ⟌8 5
    5 0   1 0 × 5
    3 5     7 × 5
      0
```
£17 each

4.
```
 2 ⟌8 8
    8 0   4 0 × 2
      8     4 × 2
      0
```
£44 each

5.
```
 4 ⟌9 2
    8 0   2 0 × 4
    1 2     3 × 4
      0
```
£23 each

6.
```
  3│9 6
    9 0    30 × 3
      6     2 × 3
      0
```
£32 each

Owl If £60 in total
The Four Multiples would earn £15 each
The Clockwise Three would earn £20 each
The Polygons would earn £12 each
The Two Co-ordinates would earn £30 each
The Four Right Angles would earn £15 each
The Fraction Boyz would earn £30 each

7.
```
      1 8
  3│5 4
```

8.
```
      2 3
  4│9 2
```

9.
```
      1 3
  5│6 5
```

10.
```
      1 3
  7│9 1
```

11.
```
      1 6
  6│9 6
```

12.
```
      2 3
  3│6 9
```

Page 72

Dividing

1.
```
      1 5 r 2
  3│4 7
    3 0    10 × 3
    1 7
    1 5     5 × 3
      2
```

2.
```
      1 6 r 2
  5│8 2
    5 0    10 × 5
    3 2
    3 0     6 × 5
      2
```

3.
```
        9 r 5
  6│5 9
    5 4     9 × 6
      5
```

4.
```
      1 8 r 1
  4│7 3
    4 0    10 × 4
    3 3
    3 2     8 × 4
      1
```

5.
```
      2 8 r 1
  2│5 7
    4 0    20 × 2
    1 7
    1 6     8 × 2
      1
```

6.
```
      1 1 r 6
  7│8 3
    7 0    10 × 7
    1 3
      7     1 × 7
      6
```

7.
```
      1 8 r 3
  4│7 5
    4 0    10 × 4
    3 5
    3 2     8 × 4
      3
```

8.
```
      1 1 r 1
  4│4 5
    4 0    10 × 4
      5
      4     1 × 4
      1
```

   9. 18 pages
10. £29·50
11. 18 teams; 9 matches
   can be played in the first round

Page 73
Fractions of amounts

1. $\frac{1}{2}$ of 8 = 4
   $\frac{1}{4}$ of 8 = 2
2. $\frac{1}{2}$ of 12 = 6
   $\frac{1}{3}$ of 12 = 4
   $\frac{1}{6}$ of 12 = 2
3. $\frac{1}{2}$ of 10 = 5
   $\frac{1}{5}$ of 10 = 2
4. $\frac{1}{2}$ of 18 = 9
   $\frac{1}{3}$ of 18 = 6
   $\frac{1}{6}$ of 18 = 3
5. $\frac{1}{3}$ of 12p = 4p
6. $\frac{1}{4}$ of 16p = 4p
7. $\frac{1}{2}$ of 10p = 5p
8. $\frac{1}{4}$ of 20p = 5p
9. $\frac{1}{3}$ of 12p = 4p
10. $\frac{1}{5}$ of 15p = 3p
11. $\frac{1}{2}$ of 14p = 7p
12. $\frac{1}{4}$ of 16p = 4p

Owl 60

Page 74
Fractions of amounts

1. $\frac{1}{2}$ of 12 = 6
2. $\frac{1}{3}$ of 9 = 3
3. $\frac{1}{4}$ of 8 = 2
4. $\frac{1}{5}$ of 15 = 3
5. $\frac{1}{2}$ of 8 = 4
6. $\frac{1}{3}$ of 18 = 6
7. $\frac{1}{4}$ of 20 = 5
8. $\frac{1}{4}$ of 16 = 4
9. $\frac{1}{3}$ of 21 = 7

Owl 2 more: 40 cubes
   4 more: 80 cubes

10. $\frac{1}{2}$ of 14 = 7
11. $\frac{1}{3}$ of 21 = 7
12. $\frac{1}{4}$ of 20 = 5
13. $\frac{1}{5}$ of 45 = 9
14. $\frac{1}{6}$ of 30 = 5
15. $\frac{1}{3}$ of 18 = 6
16. $\frac{1}{10}$ of 70 = 7
17. $\frac{1}{8}$ of 48 = 6
18. $\frac{1}{7}$ of 49 = 7
19. $\frac{1}{6}$ of 42 = 7
20. $\frac{1}{9}$ of 72 = 8
21. $\frac{1}{4}$ of 32 = 8

Page 75
Fractions of amounts

1. 16 girls
2. 24 teeth
3. 13 fruit gums
4. 2
5. 3
6. 1
7. 2
8. 6
9. 5

Owl Answers will vary.
Explore Answers will vary.
   Possible answers include:
   $\frac{1}{3}, \frac{1}{5}, \frac{1}{15}$ of 15;
   $\frac{1}{2}, \frac{1}{4}, \frac{1}{8}, \frac{1}{16}$ of 16;
   $\frac{1}{17}$ of 17;
   $\frac{1}{2}, \frac{1}{3}, \frac{1}{6}, \frac{1}{9}, \frac{1}{18}$ of 18;
   $\frac{1}{2}, \frac{1}{4}, \frac{1}{5}, \frac{1}{10}, \frac{1}{20}$ of 20;
   $\frac{1}{3}, \frac{1}{7}, \frac{1}{21}$ of 21;
   $\frac{1}{2}, \frac{1}{11}, \frac{1}{22}$ of 22;
   $\frac{1}{23}$ of 23;
   $\frac{1}{2}, \frac{1}{3}, \frac{1}{4}, \frac{1}{6}, \frac{1}{8}, \frac{1}{12}, \frac{1}{24}$ of 24;
   $\frac{1}{5}, \frac{1}{25}$ of 25

Page 76
Fractions of amounts

1. $\frac{1}{3}$ of 9 = 3→
   $\frac{2}{3}$ of 9 = 6

page 76 continued

2. $\frac{1}{4}$ of 12 = 3→
   $\frac{3}{4}$ of 12 = 9
3. $\frac{1}{5}$ of 20 = 4→
   $\frac{4}{5}$ of 20 = 16
4. $\frac{1}{6}$ of 42 = 7→
   $\frac{5}{6}$ of 42 = 35
5. $\frac{1}{10}$ of 60 = 6→
   $\frac{7}{10}$ of 60 = 42
6. $\frac{1}{8}$ of 64 = 8→
   $\frac{3}{8}$ of 64 = 24
7. $\frac{3}{5}$ of 15 = 9
8. $\frac{3}{4}$ of 28 = 21
9. $\frac{7}{10}$ of 80 = 56
10. 2
11. 11
12. 13
13. 5
14. 3
15. 26
Owl Answers will vary.

Page 77
Hundredths

1. $\frac{35}{100}$
2. $\frac{15}{100}$
3. $\frac{85}{100}$
4. $\frac{21}{100}$
5. $\frac{70}{100}$
6. $\frac{49}{100}$
7. $\frac{36}{100}$
8. $\frac{94}{100}$
9. $\frac{63}{100}$

As a decimal:
1. 0·35
2. 0·15
3. 0·85
4. 0·21
5. 0·7
6. 0·49
7. 0·36
8. 0·94
9. 0·63
10. 0·5
11. 0·25
12. 0·1
13. 0·75
14. 0·7
15. 0·2
Owl Answers will vary.
Possible answers include:
$\frac{4}{7}, \frac{5}{9}, \frac{3}{5}, \frac{6}{10}, \frac{2}{3}, \frac{4}{6}, \frac{6}{9}, \frac{5}{8}, \frac{5}{7}, \frac{3}{4}, \frac{6}{8}, \frac{7}{9}$

Page 78
Hundredths

1. 3 tenths
2. 6 hundredths
3. 3 tens or 30
4. 8 hundredths
5. 7 tenths
6. 7 hundredths
Owl Answers will vary.
Possible answers include:
5·07, 5·16, 5·25, 5·34, 5·43, 5·52, 5·61, 5·7;
6·06, 6·15, 6·24, 6·33, 6·42, 6·51, 6·6; etc.
7. a: 3·2
   b: 3·4
   c: 3·7
   d: 3·43
   e: 3·45
   f: 3·49
8. g: 11·1
   h: 11·5
   i: 11·7
   j: 11·73
   k: 11·76
   l: 11·78

As a mixed number:
7. a: $3\frac{2}{10}$
   b: $3\frac{4}{10}$
   c: $3\frac{7}{10}$
   d: $3\frac{43}{100}$

e: $3\frac{45}{100}$

f: $3\frac{49}{100}$

8. g: $11\frac{1}{10}$

h: $11\frac{5}{10}$

i: $11\frac{7}{10}$

j: $11\frac{73}{100}$

k: $11\frac{76}{100}$

l: $11\frac{78}{100}$

9. 2·35

10. 1·4

11. 6·57

12. 4·8

13. $\frac{96}{100}$

14. $2\frac{45}{100}$

15. $7\frac{31}{100}$

16. $5\frac{8}{100}$

Page 79
Hundredths

1. £6·59

2. £4·72

3. £7·25

4. £8·98

5. £3·64

6. £1·13

7. £1·13, £3·64, £4·72, £6·59, £7·25, £8·98

Owl Answers will vary.
Possible answers include:
£10, £1, 10p, £9.10, £9.01, £8.20, £8.11, £8.02 …

8. b

9. a

10. f

11. c

12. h

13. e

14. d

15. j

16. g

17. i

Owl 7: 1·51, 1·61, 1·71, 1·81, 1·91, 2·01, 2·11
2 as the hundredths digit:
6: 1·52, 1·62, 1·72, 1·82, 1·92, 2·02

Page 80
Hundredths

1. 2·85 m

2. 1·6 m

3. 4·06 m

4. 7·6 m

5. 0·94 m

6. 10·24 m

7. 10·08 m

Owl Answers will vary.

8. 80 hundredths
= 8 tenths

9. 17 tenths
= 170 hundredths

10. 320 hundredths
= 32 tenths

11. 100 tenths
= 1000 hundredths

12. 4·5

13. 4·7

14. 4·45

15. 4·45

16. 4·46

17. 4·46

18. 4·35

19. 4·22

Block AI

PCM I

3-digit numbers

1. 353
2. 466
3. 572
4. 743
5. 502
6. 430
7. 709
8. 830
9. 400
10. 396

PCM 2

4-digit numbers

1. 5327
2. 6849
3. 7503
4. 1028
5. 4610

PCM 3

5-digit numbers

1. 23 542
2. 37 460
3. 70 391
4. 45 208
5. 18 064

PCM 4

I, I0, I00, I000 more or less

1. 4647
2. 6315
3. 4078
4. 5832
5. 7407
6. 8389
7. 3154
8. 267
9. 5443
10. 6430

PCM 5

Largest, smallest and nearest number

1. 7432
2. 2358
3. 7641
4. 2483
5. 4721
6. 6843
7. 2953
8. 5126
9. 7348

PCM 6

Multiplying

1. Answer provided
2. $5 \times 4 = 20$
3. $4 \times 6 = 24$
4. $2 \times 8 = 16$
5. $6 \times 7 = 42$
6. $5 \times 5 = 25$
7. $9 \times 2 = 18$
8. $4 \times 7 = 28$
9. $7 \times 3 = 21$
10. $5 \times 8 = 40$

PCM 7

Multiplying

1. 15
2. 16
3. 70
4. 42
5. 12
6. 21

7. 54
8. 40
9. 30
10. 90
11. 18
12. 14
13. 28
14. 45
15. 80
16. 36
17. 20
18. 24
19. 35
20. 64

PCM 8
Dividing

1. Answer provided
2. $10 \div 5 = 2$
3. $12 \div 2 = 6$
4. $9 \div 3 = 3$
5. $18 \div 6 = 3$
6. $20 \div 5 = 4$
7. $15 \div 3 = 5$
8. $16 \div 4 = 4$

PCM 9
Dividing with remainders

1. Answer provided
2. 4 r 2
3. 4 r 1
4. 3 r 3
5. 3 r 2
6. 8 r 1
7. 7 r 1
8. 8 r 2
9. 6 r 3
10. 11 r 1
11. 5 r 3
12. 3 r 2
13. 9 r 1
14. 4 r 2
15. 6 r 2
16. 6 r 6

Block B1

PCM 10
Pairs to 100

1. Answer provided
2. $27 + 73 = 100$
3. $81 + 19 = 100$
4. $45 + 55 = 100$
5. $68 + 32 = 100$
6. $29 + 71 = 100$
7. $17 + 83 = 100$
8. $9 + 91 = 100$

PCM 11
Pairs to 100

1. 40
2. 82
3. 44
4. 78
5. 4
6. 26
7. 57
8. 93
9. 15
10. 42
11. 37
12. 29
13. 53
14. 62
15. 89

PCM 12
Adding to the next pound

1. 37p
2. 58p
3. 72p
4. 25p
5. 85p
6. 92p
7. 66p
8. 29p
9. 24p
10. 97p

PCM 12 continued

11. 58p
12. 11p

PCM 13
The next ten, hundred, thousand

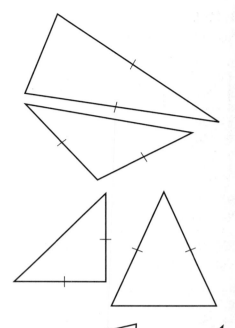

	the next ten	the next hundred	the next thousand
2574	6	26	426
5638	2	62	362
7245	5	55	755
8137	3	63	863
5946	4	54	54
3208	2	92	792
4079	1	21	921
8613	7	87	387

PCM 14
Polygons

1. triangle
2. quadrilateral
3. hexagon
4. quadrilateral
5. pentagon
6. hexagon
7. octagon
8. octagon
9. pentagon

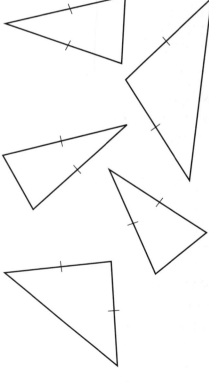

PCM 15
Isosceles triangles

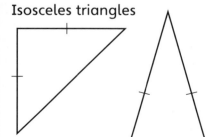

PCM 16
Isosceles triangles

1. **2.** **3.**

or   or   or

4. **5.** **6.**

or   or   or

7. **8.**

or   **9.**

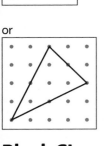

Block C1
PCM 17
Measuring lengths

A $5\frac{1}{2}$ cm
B $7\frac{1}{2}$ cm

C   7 cm
D   4 cm
E   3 cm
F   10 cm
G $8\frac{1}{2}$ cm
H   4 cm
I   11 cm

PCM 18
Millimetres, centimetres, metres and kilometres

1.   100 cm
2.   50 cm
3.   135 cm
4.   8 cm
5.   1 m
6.   5 m
7.   2 m
8.   1500 m
9.   20 mm
10.   5 mm
11.   1000 mm
12.   67 mm
13.   3500 mm
14.   2250 m

PCM 19
Ordering lengths

1.   1·47 m
2.   1·39 m
3.   2·14 m
4.   1·1 m
5.   3·5 m
6.   6·24 m
7.   0·35 m
8.   10·1 m
9.   0·35 m, 1·1 m, 1·39 m, 1·47 m, 2·14 m, 3·5 m, 6·24 m, 10·1 m
10.   8·8 cm
11.   1·46 m
12.   Parvati is not correct: 1·49 m, 1·5 m, 1·61 m, 2·01 m

PCM 20
Measuring area

A   16 squares
B   27 squares
C   9 squares
D   21 squares
E   18 squares
F   27 squares

PCM 21
Measuring area

A 13 squares
B 12 squares
C 15 squares
D 21 squares
E 9 squares
F 20 squares
G 12 squares
H 25 squares
I 18 squares
  1.   E
  2.   H

PCM 22
Tally chart

Vowel	Frequency
a	17
e	24
i	16
o	12
u	8

  1.   17
  2.   8
  3.   12
  4.   e
  5.   u
  6.   40
  7.   29
  8.   57
  9.   36

PCM 23
Frequency table

Digit	0	1	2	3	4	5	6	7	8	9
Frequency	6	4	7	4	2	6	3	3	4	5

  1.   5
  2.   2
  3.   7
  4.   4

PCM 24
Pictogram

  1.   10
  2.   17
  3.   15
  4.   6
  5.   16
  6.   32
  7.   15
  8.   21
  9.   14

PCM 25
Pictogram

  1.   6
  2.   16
  3.   13
  4.   7
  5.   9
  6.   3
  7.   9
  8.   6
  9.   7

Block D1

PCM 26
Totals

Chestertown: 27
Pontiville: 45
Nettlecombe Rangers: 43
Tunston Hill: 38

Shoremouth: 47
Aberlonian: 29
Mumberry Forest: 37
Linsham United: 34

1. Shoremouth
2. Chestertown

PCM 27
Money totals

1. 24p
2. 31p
3. 41p
4. 34p
5. 50p
6. 58p
7. Answers will vary.
8. Answers will vary.
9. Answers will vary.
10. Answers will vary.

PCM 28
Row and column totals

Upper table
Totals of rows from top to bottom:
18, 23, 24, 22
Totals of columns from left to right:
16, 24, 20, 27
Lower table
Totals of rows from top to bottom:
29, 30, 34, 25, 27
Totals of columns from left to right:
31, 28, 26, 39, 21

PCM 29
Adding and subtracting multiples of 10

1. 270
2. 370
3. 560
4. 410
5. 220
6. 540
7. 180
8. 480
9. 430
10. 630
11. 670
12. 560
13. 920
14. 310
15. 450
16. 780

PCM 30
Adding and subtracting multiples of 100

1. 500
2. 300
3. 600
4. 700
5. 700
6. 800
7. 600
8. 900
9. 700
10. 400
11. 1300
12. 1800
13. 900
14. 800

PCM 31
Analogue and digital times

1. Answer provided
2. 3:46
3. 5:09
4. 10:16
5. 8:22
6. 6:37
7. 5:47
8. 3:52
9. 4:58
10. 1:42
11. 3:34
12. 6:03

PCM 32

Minute hand

1.

| 4:43 |

2.

| 3:36 |

3.

| 6:08 |

4.

| 7:52 |

5.

| 10:43 |

6.

| 5:17 |

7.

| 9:29 |

8.

| 1:03 |

9.

| 2:13 |

10.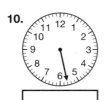

| 12:28 |

11.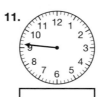

| 11:46 |

12.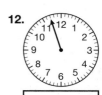

| 8:57 |

PCM 33

Minutes and seconds

1.	60 secs
2.	15 secs
3.	95 secs
4.	150 secs
5.	187 secs
6.	600 secs
7.	1 minute 30 seconds
8.	1 minute 5 seconds
9.	2 minutes 15 seconds
10.	3 minutes 20 seconds
11.	1 minute 40 seconds

Block EI

PCM 34
Sequences
1. 14, 12, 10
2. 21, 24, 27
3. 50, 45, 40
4. 400, 450, 500
5. 20, 24, 28
6. 150, 175, 200
7. 85, 80, 75
8. Answers will vary.
9. Answers will vary.

PCM 35
The next multiple

	multiple of 2	multiple of 10	multiple of 5	multiple of 3	multiple of 4
13	14	20	15	15	16
26	28	30	30	27	28
43	44	50	45	45	44
52	54	60	55	54	56
19	20	20	20	21	20
63	64	70	65	66	64

PCM 36
Division machines
1. 6, 2, 8, 3, 5, 7, 4, 9
2. 4, 6, 3, 8, 5, 2, 9, 7
3. 5, 7, 3, 9, 2, 8, 4, 6
4. 2, 6, 4, 8, 7, 3, 9, 5

PCM 37
Units digit of multiples

×1	1	2	3	4	5	6	7	8	9	0
×2	2	4	6	8	0	2	4	6	8	0
×3	3	6	9	2	5	8	1	4	7	0
×4	4	8	2	6	0	4	8	2	6	0
×5	5	0	5	0	5	0	5	0	5	0
×6	6	2	8	4	0	6	2	8	4	0
×7	7	4	1	8	5	2	9	6	3	0
×8	8	6	4	2	0	8	6	4	2	0
×9	9	8	7	6	5	4	3	2	1	0
×10	0	0	0	0	0	0	0	0	0	0

PCM 38
Fractions
1. 7 parts coloured
2. 2 parts coloured
3. 3 parts coloured
4. 5 parts coloured
5. 2 parts coloured
6. 4 parts coloured
7. 3 parts coloured
8. 7 parts coloured
9. 6 parts coloured
10. 10 parts coloured

PCM 39
Fractions
1. $\frac{1}{2}$
2. $\frac{5}{8}$
3. $\frac{3}{8}$
4. $\frac{3}{8}$
5. $\frac{1}{2}$
6. $\frac{1}{2}$
7. $\frac{3}{8}$
8. $\frac{1}{8}$

PCM 40
Mixed numbers and improper fractions
1. $2\frac{1}{3}$
2. $1\frac{3}{7}$
3. $3\frac{3}{4}$
4. $3\frac{3}{5}$
5. $13\frac{1}{2}$
6. $1\frac{5}{6}$
7. $3\frac{3}{8}$
8. $3\frac{4}{10}$ or $3\frac{2}{5}$
9. $2\frac{6}{7}$
10. $\frac{7}{2}$
11. $\frac{17}{4}$
12. $\frac{14}{3}$
13. $\frac{27}{5}$
14. $\frac{31}{3}$
15. $\frac{19}{6}$
16. $\frac{13}{5}$
17. $\frac{47}{10}$
18. $\frac{53}{8}$

PCM 4I
Matching fractions

1. $\frac{2}{6}$
2. $\frac{2}{4}$
3. $\frac{4}{6}$
4. $\frac{8}{8}$
5. $\frac{8}{16}$
6. $\frac{6}{12}$
7. $\frac{3}{4}$
8. $\frac{1}{2}$
9. $\frac{9}{12}$
10. $\frac{2}{4}$
11. $\frac{3}{4}$
12. $\frac{1}{4}$
13. $\frac{12}{16}$
14. $\frac{6}{12}$
15. $\frac{4}{12}$
16. $\frac{2}{4}$
17. $\frac{6}{6}$
18. $\frac{4}{10}$

Block A2

PCM 42
More and less

	1 more	10 less	100 more	1000 less
5836	5837	5826	5936	4836
2790	2791	2780	2890	1790
3025	3026	3015	3125	2025
4108	4109	4098	4208	3108
1893	1894	1883	1993	893
8947	8948	8937	9047	7947
5574	5575	5564	5674	4574
8049	8050	8039	8149	7049
7663	7664	7653	7763	6663
2951	2952	2941	3051	1951
3210	3211	3200	3310	2210
6499	6500	6489	6599	5499

PCM 43
Greater than, less than

1. $359 < 416$
2. $3712 < 3721$
3. $4083 < 4830$
4. $1947 < 2138$
5. $6217 < 6712$
6. $5803 > 5308$
7. $8315 < 8317$
8. $7512 > 7509$
9. $6873 > 6783$
10. $4938 < 4939$
11. $2186 > 2180$
12. $1079 < 1790$
13. $4532 > 4523$
14. $37\,186 > 35\,249$
15. $43\,874 < 45\,679$
16. $28\,136 > 28\,126$
17. $7948 > 7089$
18. $2816 > 2815$

PCM 44
Greater than, less than

1. any digit from 3 to 9
2. any digit from 0 to 6
3. 9
4. any digit from 0 to 6
5. any digit from 5 to 9
6. any digit from 1 to 6
7. any digit from 0 to 9
8. 9
9. any digit from 6 to 9
10. any digit from 0 to 9
11. any digit from 4 to 9
12. 9
13. 0
14. any digit from 0 to 7
15. any digit from 0 to 5
16. 0 or 1

PCM 45
Half-way numbers

1. 3870
2. 4175
3. 5500
4. 2900
5. 4760
6. 2650
7. 3227
8. 9550
9. 7520

PCM 46
Odd and even

1. smallest odd: 385
   smallest even: 358
   largest odd: 853
   largest even: 538
2. smallest odd: 467
   smallest even: 476
   largest odd: 647
   largest even: 764
3. smallest odd: 2385
   smallest even: 2358
   largest odd: 8523
   largest even: 8532
4. smallest odd: 4569
   smallest even: 4596
   largest odd: 9645
   largest even: 9654

PCM 47
Negative numbers

1. 14°C
2. 7°C
3. 9°C
4. 3°C
5. -5°C
6. -1°C
7. -8°C
8. -5°C
9. -11°C
10. 8°C

Block B2
PCM 48
Doubling and halving

1. 16
2. 12
3. 7
4. 9
5. 40
6. 100
7. 30
8. 40
9. 30
10. 70
11. 25
12. 45
13. 160
14. 130
15. 55
16. 60
17. 150
18. 190

PCM 49
Doubling and halving

1.

46	28	64	86	42	72	98	56	94	114

2.

42	33	24	13	34	48	37	33	46	38

PCM 50
Near doubles

1. 38 + 39 = 77
   37 + 38 = 75
   38 + 35 = 73
   38 + 41 = 79
2. 27 + 28 = 55
   27 + 25 = 52
   26 + 27 = 53
   27 + 31 = 58

PCM 50 continued

3. $87 + 89 = 176$
$87 + 86 = 173$
$85 + 87 = 172$
$86 + 88 = 174$
4. $173 + 172 = 345$
$174 + 171 = 345$
$169 + 173 = 342$
$172 + 172 = 344$
5. $457 + 458 = 915$
$457 + 455 = 912$
$459 + 457 = 916$
$452 + 458 = 910$

PCM 51
Doubling and halving

1. | 680 | 460 | 840 | 240 | 740 | 940 | 920 | 780 |
|---|---|---|---|---|---|---|---|

2. | 320 | 130 | 440 | 180 | 270 | 380 | 360 | 520 |
|---|---|---|---|---|---|---|---|

PCM 52
Dice doubling

Answers will vary.

PCM 53
Symmetrical shapes

1–3.

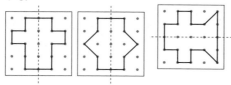

4–9. Answers will vary.

PCM 54
Shape dice

Answers will vary.

PCM 55
Net of a tetrahedron

No answers required.

Block C2
PCM 56
Litres and millilitres

1. 1000 ml
2. 500 ml
3. 2 l
4. 750 ml
5. 1500 ml
6. $\frac{1}{4}$ l
7. $6\frac{1}{2}$ l
8. 100 ml
9. 2700 ml
10. 5100 ml
11. 11 l
12. 2750 ml
13. 3500 ml
14. 10 000 ml

PCM 57
Ordering capacities

1. 1·3 l
2. 1·4 l
3. 2·1 l
4. 4·5 l
5. 3·8 l
6. 6·2 l
7. 6·15 l
8. 10·01 l
9. 1·3 l, 1·4 l, 2·1 l, 3·8 l, 4·5 l, 6·15 l, 6·2 l, 10·01 l
10. 5 full mugs, 100 ml left over
11. 4200 ml, 4·2 l
12. 4 full weeks, 100 ml left over

PCM 58
Timetable

1. 7 minutes
2. 19 minutes
3. 55 minutes
4. 34 minutes

	5.	14 minutes
	6.	40 minutes
	7.	46 minutes
	8.	41 minutes

5.	24
6.	25
7.	25
8.	23
9.	Y3: 5; Y4: 4
10.	Y3: 6; Y4: 3

PCM 59
Timetable

Answers will vary.

PCM 60
Perimeter

Shape	A	B	C	D	E	F	G	H	I	J
Perimeter in cm	8	12	16	12	16	12	14	16	12	24

PCM 6I
Rectangle areas and perimeters

1. Answers provided
2. area: $4\,cm^2$
   perimeter: 10 cm
   difference: 6 cm
3. area: $6\,cm^2$
   perimeter: 10 cm
   difference: 4 cm

d	1	2	3	4	5	6
1	3	4	5	6	7	8
2	4	4	4	4	4	4
3	5	4	3	2	1	0
4	6	4	2	0	2	4
5	7	4	1	2	5	8
6	8	4	0	4	8	12

PCM 62
Bar graphs

1. 29
2. 26
3. 28
4. 27

PCM 63
Bar graphs

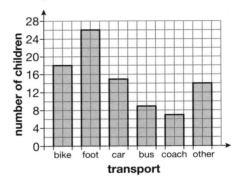

Block D2
PCM 64
Adding three numbers

1. 99
2. 88
3. 103
4. 112
5. 98
6. 165
7. 159
8. 151
9. 155
10. 140
11. 163
12. 134
13. 177
14. 178
15. 204
16. 156

PCM 65
Making totals

1. 25 + 53 + 27 = 105; or
   25 + 46 + 34 = 105
2. 31 + 53 + 27 = 111; or
   31 + 46 + 34 = 111
3. 25 + 53 + 34 = 112
4. 25 + 27 + 34 = 86
5. 42 + 53 + 46 = 141
6. 31 + 27 + 34 = 92

PCM 66
Subtracting

1. 18
2. 27
3. 34
4. 55
5. 9
6. 59
7. 16
8. 58
9. 73
10. 36
11. 35
12. 17
13. 25
14. 6
15. 28
16. 17
17. 9
18. 29

PCM 67
Problems

1. 35 weeks
2. 18 years
3. 17 boys
4. 39 chocolates
5. 18 days
6. the robin is 27 days older
7. 19 and 37
8. 24

PCM 68
Rising prices

1. 63p
2. 85p
3. 96p
4. 57p
5. 71p
6. 102p or £1·02
7. £1·55
8. £2·87

PCM 69
Adding and subtracting near multiples of 10

1. 82
2. 83
3. 67
4. 57
5. 80
6. 55
7. 161
8. 154
9. 295
10. 836
11. 244
12. 388
13. 342
14. 249
15. 571
16. 440
17. 239
18. 287

PCM 70
Adding

Children should also include estimates.
1. 481
2. 591
3. 285
4. 186
5. 374
6. 611

7. 431
8. 775
9. 723
10. 333
11. 610
12. 841

PCM 7I
Adding 3-digit numbers
Answers will vary.

Block E2
PCM 72
Sixes

1	2	3	4	5	6
7	8	9	10	11	12
13	14	15	16	17	18
19	20	21	22	23	24
25	26	27	28	29	30
31	32	33	34	35	36
37	38	39	40	41	42
43	44	45	46	47	48
49	50	51	52	53	54
55	56	57	58	59	60

6	12	18	24	30	36	42	48	54	60

PCM 73
Multiplying and dividing by 6
1. 30
2. 18
3. 10
4. 5
5. 42
6. 4
7. 36
8. 3
9. 24

10. 54
11. 8
12. 6
13. 12
14. 9
15. 48
16. 60
17. 7
18. 2

PCM 74
Eights

1	2	3	4	5	6	7	8
9	10	11	12	13	14	15	16
17	18	19	20	21	22	23	24
25	26	27	28	29	30	31	32
33	34	35	36	37	38	39	40
41	42	43	44	45	46	47	48
49	50	51	52	53	54	55	56
57	58	59	60	61	62	63	64
65	66	67	68	69	70	71	72
73	74	75	76	77	78	79	80

8	16	24	32	40	48	56	64	72	80

PCM 75
Multiplying and dividing by 8
1. 16
2. 56
3. 10
4. 5
5. 72
6. 64
7. 3
8. 2
9. 7
10. 24
11. 4
12. 80
13. 6
14. 40

15. 32
16. 9
17. 48
18. 8

PCM 76
Multiplying by 8, 80 and 800

1. 56; 560
2. 40; 400
3. 72; 720
4. 320
5. 640
6. 2400
7. 4800
8. 1600
9. 5600
10. 4000
11. 7200
12. 320
13. 560

PCM 77
Fractions on a number line

1. $\frac{1}{3}, \frac{2}{3}$
2. $\frac{1}{2}, \frac{3}{4}$
3. $\frac{2}{5}, \frac{4}{5}$
4. $\frac{1}{6}, \frac{5}{6}$
5. $\frac{1}{8}, \frac{3}{8}, \frac{5}{8}, \frac{7}{8}$

PCM 78
Comparing fractions

1. $\frac{1}{4} < \frac{1}{2}$
2. $\frac{1}{3} > \frac{1}{4}$
3. $\frac{2}{3} < \frac{3}{4}$
4. $\frac{1}{4} < \frac{3}{8}$
5. $\frac{5}{6} > \frac{3}{4}$
6. $\frac{5}{8} < \frac{2}{3}$
7. $\frac{7}{12} > \frac{1}{2}$
8. $\frac{8}{12} = \frac{2}{3}$
9. $\frac{5}{12} < \frac{3}{6}$
10. $\frac{3}{4} = \frac{9}{12}$

11. $\frac{2}{6} = \frac{4}{12}$
12. $\frac{3}{8} > \frac{1}{3}$

PCM 79
Mixed numbers

1. Answer provided
2. Answer provided
3. $2\frac{7}{10}$
4. 2·7
5. $1\frac{8}{10}$
6. 1·8
7. $4\frac{2}{10}$; or $4\frac{1}{5}$
8. 4·2
9. $3\frac{1}{10}$
10. 3·1
11. $\frac{9}{10}$
12. 0·9

PCM 80
Weighing scales

1. Answer provided
2. 7·4 kg
3. 1·9 kg
4. 6·3 kg
5. 3·7 kg
6. 8·5 kg
7. 2·8 kg
8. 6·6 kg
9. 9·1 kg

PCM 81
Measuring lengths

1. 4·8 cm
2. 3·6 cm
3. 4·8 cm
4. 8·4 cm
5. 7·0 cm
6. 2·9 cm
7. 10·1 cm
8. 5·3 cm

Block A3

PCM 82

Rounding

1. position: 74, 78, 83, 86, 89
   nearest 10: 70, 80, 80, 90, 90
2. position: 203, 207, 211, 215, 218
   nearest 10: 200, 210, 210, 220, 220
3. position: 128, 134, 144, 156, 168
   nearest 10: 130, 130, 140, 160, 170

PCM 83

Rounding

1. 237 or 238
2. 372
3. 327 or 328
4. 278 or 283
5. 872 or 873
6. 738
7. 273
8. 382 or 378
9. 823
10. 782 or 783
11. 387
12. 837
13. 728 or 732
14. 287

PCM 84

Rounding money

Amount	Nearest 10p	Nearest £1
£4·27	£4·30	£4·00
£3·62	£3·60	£4·00
£7·48	£7·50	£7·00
£5·12	£5·10	£5·00
£1·01	£1·00	£1·00
£6·38	£6·40	£6·00
£2·15	£2·20	£2·00
£8·74	£8·70	£9·00
£14·55	£14·60	£15·00
£7·26	£7·30	£7·00
£11·53	£11·50	£12·00
£3·97	£4·00	£4·00

PCM 85

Multiplying and dividing by 10 and 100

1. 70
2. 310
3. 500
4. 1700
5. 420
6. 3600
7. 1700
8. 6000
9. 110
10. 1200
11. 40
12. 27
13. 30
14. 18
15. 68
16. 9
17. 43
18. 270
19. 6400
20. 750

PCM 86

Multiplying by 5 and 20

1. $24 \times 10 = 240$;
   $24 \times 5 = 120$
2. $66 \times 10 = 660$;
   $66 \times 5 = 330$
3. $42 \times 10 = 420$;
   $42 \times 20 = 840$
4. $18 \times 10 = 180$;
   $18 \times 20 = 360$
5. $63 \times 10 = 630$;
   $63 \times 5 = 315$
6. $47 \times 10 = 470$;
   $47 \times 20 = 940$
7. $82 \times 10 = 820$;
   $82 \times 20 = 1640$
8. $73 \times 10 = 730$;
   $73 \times 5 = 365$

9. $56 \times 10 = 560;$
    $56 \times 5 = 280$
10. $29 \times 10 = 290;$
    $29 \times 20 = 580$

PCM 87

Making 100

1. Answer provided
2. 50
3. 25
4. 20
5. 10
6. 5
7. 4
8. 2
9. 500
10. 1000
11. 2000
12. 200
13. Answers will vary.
14. Answers will vary.
15. Answers will vary.

PCM 88

Subtracting

1. Answer provided
2.
```
    1 4 2
  -   5 7
          3 →     6 0
        8 0 → 1 4 0
          2 → 1 4 2
        8 5
```

3.
```
    1 2 3
  -   3 9
          1 →     4 0
        8 0 → 1 2 0
          3 → 1 2 3
        8 4
```

4.
```
    3 2 4
  - 1 5 6
          4 → 1 6 0
        1 6 0 → 3 2 0
          4 → 3 2 4
        1 6 8
```

5.
```
    2 3 1
  - 1 8 5
          5 → 1 9 0
        4 0 → 2 3 0
          1 → 2 3 1
        4 6
```

6.
```
    4 1 3
  - 2 2 7
          3 → 2 3 0
        1 8 0 → 4 1 0
          3 → 4 1 3
        1 8 6
```

7.
```
    2 4 5
  - 1 6 8
          2 → 1 7 0
        7 0 → 2 4 0
          5 → 2 4 5
        7 7
```

8.
```
    3 3 4
  - 1 5 9
          1 → 1 6 0
        1 7 0 → 3 3 0
          4 → 3 3 4
        1 7 5
```

9.
```
    5 2 1
  - 3 7 4
          6 → 3 8 0
        1 4 0 → 5 2 0
          1 → 5 2 1
        1 4 7
```

PCM 89

Subtracting

Children should also include estimates.

1. 61
2. 26
3. 59

4. 56
5. 17
6. 25
7. 18
8. 34
9. 59

PCM 90
Subtracting

Children should also include estimates.
1. 441
2. 351
3. 213
4. 373
5. 152
6. 239
7. 257
8. 368
9. 326

PCM 91
Dice subtractions

Answers will vary.

Block B3
PCM 92
Differences

1. 2003 − 1996 = 7
2001 − 1995 = 6
2011 − 1995 = 16
2005 − 1987 = 18
2. 5001 − 4996 = 5
5007 − 4995 = 12
5013 − 4994 = 19
5003 − 4986 = 17
3. 3901 − 3892 = 9
3907 − 3896 = 11
3912 − 3897 = 15
3904 − 3889 = 15

PCM 93
Multiplying and dividing by 9

1. 45
2. 27
3. 10
4. 2
5. 63
6. 5
7. 72
8. 6
9. 9
10. 90
11. 3
12. 18
13. 54
14. 4
15. 81
16. 8
17. 7
18. 36

PCM 94
Nines digits

×9 table	Digit total	Digit difference
2 × 9 = 18	9	7
3 × 9 = 27	9	5
4 × 9 = 36	9	3
5 × 9 = 45	9	1
6 × 9 = 54	9	1
7 × 9 = 63	9	3
8 × 9 = 72	9	5
9 × 9 = 81	9	7
10 × 9 = 90	9	9

PCM 95
Nines digits

1. 36
2. 72
3. 81
4. 45

5. 90
6. 54
7. 63
8. 27
9. 18
10. 441
11. 630
12. 522
13. 108
14. 216
15. 324
16. 531
17. 333
18. 675

PCM 96
Compass directions

1. Answer provided
2. W
3. S
4. SE
5. E
6. NE
7. NW
8. W
9. SW
10. SE

PCM 97
Compass directions

1. house
2. train
3. flag or house
4. windmill
5. tree
6. castle
7. cart or bicycle
8. windmill

PCM 98
Directions

No answers required.

PCM 99
Right angles

1. 1
2. 3
3. 2
4. $\frac{1}{2}$
5. 4
6. $2\frac{1}{2}$
7. $3\frac{1}{2}$
8. $1\frac{1}{2}$
9. 0

PCM 100
Angles in shapes

a 90°
b 45°
c 135°
d 90°
e 270°
f 315°
g 45°
h 135°

Block C3
PCM 101
Weight

1. 1 kg
2. 500 g
3. 2000 g
4. 250 g
5. $\frac{3}{4}$ kg
6. $\frac{4}{10}$ kg
7. 100 g
8. 3750 g

9. 2300 g
10. 5800 g
11. $8\frac{1}{2}$ kg
12. 12 kg
13. 1100 g
14. 2500 g

PCM 102
Estimating weights

Answers will vary.

PCM 103
Ordering weights

1. 1·4 kg
2. 1·3 kg
3. 2·1 kg
4. 5·1 kg
5. 3·5 kg
6. 6·2 kg
7. 0·75 kg
8. 10·1 kg
9. 0·75 kg, 1·3 kg, 1·4 kg, 2·1 kg, 3·5 kg, 5·1 kg, 6·2 kg, 10·1 kg
10. 14·5 kg
11. 3·9 kg, 4·3 kg, 4·6 kg
12. 6 kg

PCM 104
Coordinates

A   (3, 1)
B   (2, 4)
C   (7, 5)
D   (1, 2)
E   (8, 0)
F   (6, 2)
G   (4, 6)
H   (1, 8)
I   (0, 5)
J   (5, 3)

PCM 105
Coordinates

1. square
2. equilateral triangle
3. pentagon
4. heptagon
5. rectangle
6. hexagon
7. octagon
8. isosceles triangle
9. irregular hexagon
10. circle

PCM 106
Coordinate shapes

1.

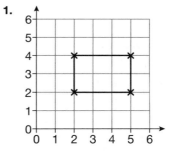

2.

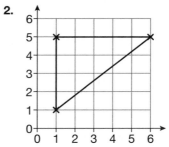

3.

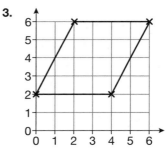

PCM 106 continued

4.

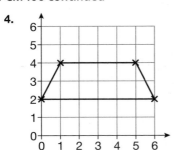

1. rectangle
2. triangle
3. quadrilateral
4. quadrilateral

PCM 107
Calendars

September						
M	**Tu**	**W**	**Th**	**F**	**Sa**	**Su**
		1	2	3	4	5
6	7	8	9	10	11	12
13	14	15	16	17	18	19
20	21	22	23	24	25	26
27	28	29	30			

October						
M	**Tu**	**W**	**Th**	**F**	**Sa**	**Su**
				1	2	3
4	5	6	7	8	9	10
11	12	13	14	15	16	17
18	19	20	21	22	23	24
25	26	27	28	29	30	31

November						
M	**Tu**	**W**	**Th**	**F**	**Sa**	**Su**
1	2	3	4	5	6	7
8	9	10	11	12	13	14
15	16	17	18	19	20	21
22	23	24	25	26	27	28
29	30					

December						
M	**Tu**	**W**	**Th**	**F**	**Sa**	**Su**
		1	2	3	4	5
6	7	8	9	10	11	12
13	14	15	16	17	18	19
20	21	22	23	24	25	26
27	28	29	30	31		

PCM 108
Calendars

1. Friday
2. Thursday
3. Tuesday
4. Tuesday
5. Tuesday
6. Thursday
7. Saturday
8. Sunday
9. 7th
10. 18th
11. 12th
12. 26th
13. 24th

PCM 109
Calendar patterns

Answers will vary.

PCM 110
Venn diagrams

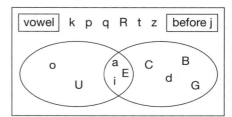

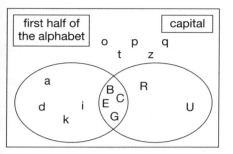

first half of the alphabet

capital

o   p   q
t   z

a
d   i
k

B
E C
G

R

U

PCM 111

Carroll diagrams

1.

	even	odd
multiple of 5	10 20 50	5 15
not a multiple of 5	6 18 22	9 13 21

2.

	digit total less than 10	digit total not less than 10
even	14 32 42 60	28 48 56 74
odd	17 35 81	55 75 95

3.

	multiple of 3	not a multiple of 3
multiple of 2	6 18 42	4 8 14 28 32
not a multiple of 2	3 15 21	7 11 13 17 23

Block D3
PCM 112
Adding

Children should also include estimates.
1. £6·21
2. £6·04
3. £8·13
4. £7·14
5. £9·32
6. £4·64
7. £12·69
8. £12·26
9. £14·55

PCM 113
Checking our calculations

1. ✓
2. £7·82 + £6·77 = £14·49
3. ✓
4. £4·68 + £6·73 = £11·41
5. £5·91 + £6·15 = £12·06
6. ✓
7. ✓
8. ✓
9. £8·19 + £4·78 = £12·97
10. ✓

Adam scored 6 out of 10

Claire spent £28·45 + £41·78
Gemma spent £32·67 + £41·78
Duncan spent £32·67 + £37·89

PCM 114
Subtracting

Children should also include estimates.
1. £3·45
2. £1·23
3. £2·57
4. £2·86
5. £1·65
6. £4·42
7. £3·75
8. £2·86
9. £2·48

PCM 115
Sevens
1. 21
2. 56
3. 10
4. 2
5. 9
6. 5
7. 70
8. 4
9. 8
10. 42
11. 49
12. 28
13. 63
14. 6
15. 14
16. 3
17. 7
18. 35

PCM 116
Sevens and nines
No answers required.

PCM 117
Multiplying
Answers will vary.

PCM 118
Multiplying

1.

7	30	2
	210	14

$$32 \times 7 = 224$$

210
+ 14
224

2.

8	40	3
	320	24

$$43 \times 8 = 344$$

320
+ 24
344

3.

9	60	4
	540	36

$$64 \times 9 = 576$$

540
+ 36
576

4.

4	20	8
	80	32

$$28 \times 4 = 112$$

80
+ 32
112

5.

6	20	6
	120	36

$$26 \times 6 = 156$$

120
+ 36
156

6.

9	30	5
	270	45

$$35 \times 9 = 315$$

270
+ 45
315

7.

7	50	9
	350	63

$$59 \times 7 = 413$$

350
+ 63
413

8.

5	80	7
	400	35

$$87 \times 5 = 435$$

400
+ 35
435

Block E3

PCM 119
Multiplying
Children should also include estimates.
1. 72
2. 152
3. 413
4. 340
5. 424
6. 282
7. 384
8. 315
9. 243

PCM 120
Multiplying
Answers will vary.

PCM 121
Multiplying
Answers will vary.

PCM 122
Dividing

1. Answer provided

2.
```
      1 9
  2 | 3 8
      2 0    1 0 × 2
      1 8      9 × 2
        0    1 9
```

3.
```
      1 8
  4 | 7 2
      4 0    1 0 × 4
      3 2      8 × 4
        0    1 8
```

4.
```
      1 7
  5 | 8 5
      5 0    1 0 × 5
      3 5      7 × 5
        0    1 7
```

5.
```
      1 6
  6 | 9 6
      6 0    1 0 × 6
      3 6      6 × 6
        0    1 6
```

6.
```
      1 6
  3 | 4 8
      3 0    1 0 × 3
      1 8      6 × 3
        0    1 6
```

7.
```
      1 3
  7 | 9 1
      7 0    1 0 × 7
      2 1      3 × 7
        0    1 3
```

8.
```
      1 4
  4 | 5 6
      4 0    1 0 × 4
      1 6      4 × 4
        0    1 4
```

9.
```
      1 4
  6 | 8 4
      6 0    1 0 × 6
      2 4      4 × 6
        0    1 4
```

PCM 123
Fractions of money

1. 9p
2. 7p
3. 8p
4. 5p
5. 11p
6. 7p
7. 6p
8. 4p
9. 7p
10. 3p
11. 9p
12. 8p
13. 9p
14. 11p
15. 8p
16. 9p

PCM 124
Fractions of weights

1. 8 kg
2. 6 kg
3. 8 kg
4. 10 kg
5. 9 kg
6. 6 kg
7. 24 kg
8. 35 kg
9. 15 kg
10. 20 kg
11. 20 kg
12. 15 kg
13. 8 kg
14. 9 kg

PCM I25
Hundredths

A	Answer provided
B	5·36
C	5·45
D	5·54
E	5·71
F	5·87
G	7·08
H	7·31
I	7·4
J	7·54
K	7·72
L	7·94
M	13·14
N	13·31
O	13·49
P	13·65
Q	13·82
R	13·96

PCM I26
Hundredths

Answers will vary.

PCM I27
Hundredths

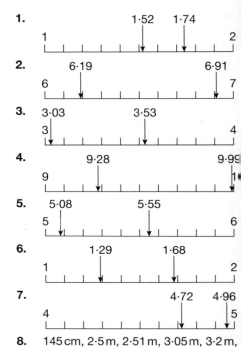

8. 145 cm, 2·5 m, 2·51 m, 3·05 m, 3·2 m, 5·71 m